The Bunyan Collection by Reformation Press

Reformation Press

160 37th Street
Lindenhurst, NewYork 11701 USA
516. 956. 0606
reformationpress@email.com
www.reformationpress.com

ISBN 0-9670840-2-4

Cover Design by Michael Rotolo

Manufactured in the United States of America
2 3 4 5 6 7 8 9 10 02 03

A PUBLICATION OF

REFORMATION PRESS

THE

Pilgrim's Progreſs

FROM

THIS WORLD,

TO

That which is to come:

Delivered under the Similitude of a

DREAM

Wherein is Diſcovered,
The manner of his ſetting out,
His Dangerous Journey, And ſafe
Arrival at the Deſired Countrey.

I have uſed Similitudes, Hoſ. 12:10.

By *John Bunyan.*

Licenſed and Entred according to Order.

LONDON

Printed for *Nath. Ponder* at the *Peacock*
in the *Poultrey* near *Cornhil*, 1678.

Original Title Page, First Edition

The Sleeping Portrait

Engraved by Robert White, it was most likely intended for the first edition of 1678, though withdrawn due to the name 'Destruction' being incorrectly titled 'Vanity'. The above corrected picture was included in the third edition of 1679.

Principles of the
ACCURATE REVISED TEXT

1. The basis of this revision is the definitive text of *The Pilgrim's Progress* edited by J. B. Wharey and Roger Sharrock, and published by Oxford Press (Clarendon) in 1960.
2. Of foremost consideration has been a style of simple conversational English that, while not being racy, yet maintains faithfulness to the style, meaning, doctrine, and purposes of John Bunyan. This editor welcomes suggestions and constructive criticism in this regard.
3. A select variety of archaisms has been retained, with modern equivalent terms in brackets, since these expressions have gained a particular timeless quality and quaintness about them that are intrinsic to *The Pilgrim's Progress*. Certain other antiquated modes of sentence construction have been modified to produce a more contemporary style of expression.
4. Chapter headings, as well as occasional subdivisions, have been added to assist in the understanding of *The Pilgrim's Progress*.
5. The marginal Scripture references and most notations included by John Bunyan have been retained as footnotes and also revised. In certain instances, where an item appears to be redundant, the notation has been excluded. Of course the text includes countless other allusions to Bible passages, and a number of these are referenced in italics as footnotes. Some additional clarifying comments on the text have been added as well.

Barry E. Horner

TABLE OF CONTENTS

INTRODUCTION

URING the latter half of this twentieth century, numerous revisions of *The Pilgrim's Progress* have been published. However, while several of these publications have proved to be accurate and useful, many have been lacking in precision, not only in linguistic style, but also with regard to the author's doctrinal intentions.

Doubtless John Bunyan would have heartily agreed that his allegory should be made as clear as is possible to this modern generation, though without sacrificing truth and his attractive plainness of writing.

With this in mind, yet another contemporary rendering is offered with the earnest desire that it will prove faithful to the Bedford tinker's expressed purpose, namely that the reader perceive the substance of Bible and gospel truth that lies beyond the veil of allegorical style.

Barry E. Horner

THE AUTHOR'S APOLOGY FOR HIS BOOK

WHEN at first I took my pen in hand,
To write this way, I did not understand
That I at all should make a little book
In such a style; no, I had undertook
To make another, which when almost done,[1]
Before I was aware, I this begun.

And so it was: I writing of the way
And race of saints in this our gospel day,
Fell suddenly into an allegory[2]
About their journey, and the way to glory,
In more than twenty things, which I set down;
This done, I twenty more had in my crown,
And they again began to multiply,
Like sparks that from the coals of fire do fly.
Then no, I thought since if you breed so fast,
I'll put you by yourself, lest you at last
Should prove ad infinitum, and eat out
The book that I already am about.

Well, so I did; but yet I did not think
To show to all the world my pen and ink
In such a style; I only thought to make
I knew not what, nor did I undertake
Thereby to please my neighbor; no, not I,
I did it my own self to gratify.

---

1 *Probably The Heavenly Footman based on I Corinthians 9:24.*

2 *Bunyan also refers to his allegorical style, in this and his concluding poem, as similitude, metaphor, parable, figure, type, fable, and shadow.*

Neither did I but vacant seasons spend
In this my scribble; nor did I intend
But to divert myself in doing this,
From worser thoughts which make me do amiss.

Thus I set pen to paper with delight,
And quickly had my thoughts in black and white.
For having now my method by the end [*tail*],
Still as I pulled it came,[3] and so I penned
It down, until it came at last to be
For length and breadth the bigness that you see.

Well, when I had thus put my ends together,
I showed them others, that I might see whether
They would condemn them, or them justify:
And some said, "Let them live"; some, "Let them die";
Some said, "*John*, print it"; others said, "Not so";
Some said, "It might do good"; others said, "No".

Now was I in a straight [*plight*], and did not see
Which was the best thing to be done by me;
At last I thought, since you are thus divided,
I will print it, and so the case decided.

For, thought I, some I see would have it done,
Though others in that channel do not run.
To prove then who advised for the best,
Thus I thought fit to put it to the test.

I further thought, if now I did deny
Those that would have it thus, to gratify,
I did not know, but hinder them I might,
Of that which would to them be great delight.

For those that were not for its coming forth,
I said to them, "Offend you I am loath;
Yet since your brethren pleased with it be.
Forbear to judge till you do further see."

---

3 *Bunyan is probably alluding to a woman pulling thread from a spinning-wheel.*

If that you will not read, let it alone;
Some love the meat, some love to pick the bone:
Yes, that I might them better palliate,
I did too with them thus expostulate.

May I not write in such a style as this?
In such a method too, and yet not miss
Mine end, your good? Why may it not be done?
Dark clouds bring waters, when the bright bring none;
Yes, dark or bright, if they their silver drops
Cause by descent, the earth to yielding crops,
Give praise to both, and carpeth [*censure*] not at
either,
But treasure up the fruit they yield together;
Yes, so combine them both, that in her fruit
None can distinguish this from that, they suit
Her well when hungry; but if she be full
She spews out both, and makes their blessings null.

You see the ways the fisherman does take
To catch the fish, what engines he does make?
Behold! how he engages all his wits,
Also his snares, lines, angles, hooks and nets.
Yet fish there be, that neither hook nor line,
Nor snare, nor net, nor engine can make thine;
They must be groped for, and be tickled too,
Or they will not be caught, whate'er you do.[4]

How does the fowler seek to catch his game?
By varied means, all which one cannot name.
His gun, his nets, his lime-twigs,[5] light and bell;
He creeps, he goes, he stands; yes, who can tell
Of all his postures? Yet there's none of these
Will make him master of what fowls he please.
Yes, he must pipe, and whistle to catch this;
Yet if he does so, that bird he will miss.

---

[4] *Matt. 4:19.*

[5] *Twigs smeared with sticky birdlime used to snare small birds.*

If that a pearl may in a toad's head dwell,[6]
And may be found too, in an oyster-shell;
If things that promise nothing, do contain
What better is than gold; who will disdain
(That have an inkling of it) there to look,
That they may find it? Now my little book,
(Though void of all those paintings that may make
It with this or the other man to take,)
Is not without those things that do excel,
What do in brave but empty notions dwell.

"Well, yet I am not fully satisfied, that
This your book will stand when soundly tried."
Why, what's the matter? "It is dark [*obscure*]",[7] What though?
"But it is feigned [*fiction*]." What if that is so?
Some men by words of fiction, dark as mine,
Make truth to spangle, and its rays to shine.
"But they lack solidness." Speak man your mind;
"They drowned the weak; metaphors make us blind."

Solidity, indeed becomes the pen
Of him that writes things divine to men;
But must I needs lack solidness, because
By metaphors I speak; were not *God's* laws,
His gospel laws in olden time held forth
By types, shadows and metaphors? Yet loath
Will any sober man be to find fault
With them, lest he be found for to assault
The highest wisdom. No, he rather stoops,
And seeks to find out what by pins and loops,
By calves and sheep, by heifers and by rams,
By birds and herbs, and by the blood of lambs;
God speaks to him, and happy is he
That finds the light and grace that in them be.

---

6 *An allusion to the mythical belief that certain precious gems were formed in the head of a toad.*

7 *Ps. 78:2.*

Be not too forward therefore to conclude
That I lack solidness, that I am rude [*superficial*];
All things solid in show not solid be;
All things in parables despise not we,
Lest things more hurtful lightly we receive,
And things that good are, of our souls bereave.

My dark and cloudy words they do but hold
The truth, as cabinets enclose the gold.
The prophets used much by metaphors
To set forth truth; yes, who so considers
Christ, his Apostles too, shall plainly see,
That truths to this day in such garments be.

Am I afraid to say that holy writ,
Which for its style and phrase puts down [*quells*]
all wit,
Is everywhere so full of all these things,
Dark figures, allegories? Yet there springs
From that same book that luster, and those rays
Of light that turns our darkest nights to days.

Come, let my carper [*critic*] to his life now look,
And find there darker lines than in my book
He finds any. Yes, and let him know
That in his best things there are worse lines too.

May we but stand before impartial men,
To his poor one, I dare adventure ten,
That they will take my meaning in these lines
Far better than his lies in silver shrines.[8]
Come, truth, although in swaddling-clothes,[9] I find
Informs the judgment, rectifies the mind,
Pleases the understanding, makes the will
Submit; the memory too it does fill
With what our imagination does please;
Likewise, it tends our troubles to appease.

---

8 *Acts 19:24.*

9 *Infant or allegorical dress.*

Sound words I know *Timothy* is to use,[10]
And old wives' fables he is to refuse;[11]
But yet grave *Paul* him nowhere does forbid
The use of parables; in which lay hid
That gold, those pearls, and precious stones that were
Worth digging for, and that with greatest care.

Let me add one more word, O man of *God*![12]
Are you offended? Do you wish I had
Put forth my matter in another dress,
Or that I had in things been more express?
Three things let me propound, then I submit
To those that are my betters, as is fit.

1. I find not that I am denied the use
Of this my method, so I no abuse
Put on the words, things, readers, or be rude
In handling figure, or similitude,
In application; but, all that I may,
Seek the advance of truth this or that way.
Denied did I say? No, I have leave,
(Example too, and that from them that have
God better pleased by their words or ways,
Than any man that breathes nowadays),
Thus to express my mind, thus to declare
Things unto you that more excellent are.

2. I find that men, as high as trees, will write
Dialogue-wise; yet no man does them slight
For writing so; indeed if they abuse
Truth, cursed be they, and the craft they use
To that intent; but yet let truth be free
To make her sallies [*charges*] upon you and me,
Which way it pleases *God*. For who knows how,
Better than he that taught us first to plough,

---

10 *II Tim. 1:13.*

11 *I Tim. 4:7.*

12 *I Tim. 6:11. Bunyan's objectors were most likely pastors.*

To guide our mind and pens for his design?
And he makes base things usher in divine.

3. I find that holy writ in many places
Has likeness with this method, where the cases
Do call for one thing to set forth another;
Use it I may then, and yet nothing smother
Truth's golden beams; no, by this method may
Make it cast forth its rays as light as day.

And now before I do put up my pen,
I'll show the profit of my book, and then
Commit both you and it unto that hand
That pulls the strong down, and makes weak ones stand.

This book it chalks [*marks*] out before your eyes,
The man that seeks the everlasting prize;[13]
It shows you whence he comes, where he goes,
What he leaves undone, also what he does;
It also shows you how he runs and runs,
Till he unto the gate of glory comes.

It shows too, who sets out for life amain [*vigorously*],
As if the lasting crown they would attain;
Here also you may see the reason why
They lose their labor, and like fools do die.

This book will make a traveler of you,
If by its counsel you its rules will do;
It will direct you to the *Holy Land*,
If you will its directions understand;
Yes, it will make the slothful active be,
The blind also delightful things to see.

Are you for something rare, and profitable?
Would you see a truth within a fable?
Are you forgetful? Would you remember
From New Year's day to the last of December?
Then read my fancies, they will stick like burs,
And may be to the helpless, comforters.

---

13 *I Cor. 9:24; Phil. 3:14.*

This book is writ in such a dialect
As may the minds of listless men affect:
It seems a novelty, and yet contains
Nothing but sound and honest gospel strains.

Would you divert yourself from melancholy?
Would you be pleasant, yet be far from folly?
Would you read riddles and their explanation?
Or else be drowned in your contemplation?
Do you love picking meat? Or would you view
A man in the clouds, and hear him speak to you?
Would you be in a dream, and yet not sleep?[14]
Or would you in a moment laugh and weep?
Would you lose yourself, and catch no harm?
And find yourself again without a charm?
Would read yourself, and read you know not what
And yet know whether you are blest or not,
By reading the same lines? Oh then come hither,
And lay my book, your head and heart together.

JOHN BUNYAN

Christian

[14] *Search for the paradox of reality in an allegory.*

THE PILGRIM'S PROGRESS
in the similitude of a
DREAM

1

CHRISTIAN FLEES FROM THE CITY OF DESTRUCTION

AS I walked through the wilderness of this world, I came upon a certain place where there was a den;[1] and I lay down in that place to sleep; and as I slept I dreamed a dream.

I dreamed, and behold I saw a man clothed in rags[2] standing in a certain place, with his face [*turned away*] from his own house, a book in his hand, and a great burden on his back. I looked and saw him open the book, and read therein; and as he read, he wept and trembled: and not being able to contain himself any longer, he broke out with a lamentable cry, saying,"What shall I do?"[3]

Therefore in this plight he went home, and restrained himself as long as he could, so that his wife and children would not notice his distress. But he could not be silent long for the reason that his trouble increased. Therefore at length he broke his mind to his wife and children; and thus he began to talk to them. "Oh my dear wife," he said, "and you the children of my bowels [*deepest affections*], I your dear friend am myself undone [*crushed*], by reason of a burden that weighs heavily upon me: moreover, I am certainly informed that this our city will be burned with fire from *Heaven*, in which fearful overthrow, both

---

1 Bedford jail.

2 Isa. 64:6; Ps. 38:4; Hab. 2:2; Luke 14:33.

3 Acts 16:30-31.

myself, with you my wife and sweet babes, shall come to a miserable ruin, except (which alternative is not apparent) some way of escape can be found, whereby we may be delivered."

At this these close relatives of his were greatly amazed. It was not that they believed to be true what he said to them, but rather because they thought that some frenzy distemper [*disorientating disease*] had got into his head. Consequently, with the night approaching, and with the hope that sleep might settle his brains, they got him to bed with all haste. However instead of sleeping, he spent that evening in sighs and tears.

So when the morning was come, they enquired as to how he was feeling, and he told them, "Worse and worse." He also intended to talk to them again, but they began to firmly resist him. They also contrived to drive away his demented frame of mind by means of surly carriages toward him [*responding with contemptuous and irritating behavior*]. Sometimes they would deride, sometimes they would chide, and at other times they would quite neglect him.[4] Therefore he began to retire to his bedroom to pray for and pity them, and also condole [*lament*] over his misery. He would also walk alone in the nearby fields, sometimes reading and sometimes praying; and so for some days he spent his time in this manner.

Now I noticed on a particular occasion, when he was walking in the fields, that he was (according to his habit) reading in his book, and greatly distressed in his mind; and as he read, he burst out, as he had done before, crying, "What shall I do to be saved?"[5]

I also saw that he looked this way and that way, as if he would run; yet he stood still because, as I perceived, he could not tell which way to go. I then looked and saw a man named *Evangelist*[6] coming to him who asked, "For what reason are you crying?" He answered, "Sir, I understand by the book in my hand that I am condemned to die, and after that to come to

---

4 Carnal medication for a sick soul.

5 *Acts 2:37; 16:30.*

6 *Representing Pastor John Gifford, who greatly helped Bunyan at his time of conversion.*

judgment;[7] and I find that I am not willing to do the first,[8] nor able to do the second."[9]

Then said *Evangelist*, "Why are you not willing to die since this life is accompanied with so many evils?" The man answered, "Because I fear that this burden that is upon my back will sink me lower than the grave; and I shall fall into *Tophet* [*a place of burning*].[10] And sir, if I am not fit to go to prison, I am quite sure I am not fit to go to judgment, and as a consequence to execution, and the thoughts of these things make me cry."

Then said *Evangelist*, "If this is your condition, then why are you standing still?" He answered, "Because I do not know which way to go." Then *Evangelist* gave him a parchment scroll[11] on which was written within, "Fly from the wrath to come."[12]

Therefore the man read the scroll, and looking upon *Evangelist* very carefully, said, "Which way must I go to escape?" Then said *Evangelist*, pointing with his finger beyond a very large field, "Do you see a *Wicket-gate* [*small gate*][13] over there?" The man replied, "No." Then he was asked, "Do you see a shining light[14] not quite so far away?" He said, "I think I do." Then said *Evangelist*, "Keep that light before your eye, and go directly toward it, and then you shall see the gate,[15] at which, when you knock, you will be told what you are to do."

So I saw in my dream that the man began to run. Now he had not run far from his own door when his wife and children, perceiving his departure, began to cry out to him so that he

---

7 Heb. 9:27.

8 Job 16:21-22.

9 Ezek. 22:14.

10 Isa. 30:33.

11 Conviction of the necessity of flying.

12 Matt. 3:7.

13 Matt. 7:13-14. *It was usually beside or in a larger gate.*

14 Ps. 119:105; II Pet. 1:19.

15 Christ and the way to him cannot be found without the Word.

might return. But the man put his fingers in his ears[16] and ran on crying, "Life, life, eternal life."[17] So he did not look behind him,[18] but rather fled toward the middle of the plain.

Evangelist

---

[16] Luke 14:26.

[17] *John 3:16, 36.*

[18] Gen. 19:17, *cf. v.* 26.

2

CHRISTIAN IS PURSUED BY OBSTINATE AND PLIABLE

THE neighbors also came out to see him run;[1] and as he ran, some mocked, others threatened; and some cried for him to return. Now among those that did so, there were two that were determined to fetch him back by force. The name of one was *Obstinate*, and the name of the other was *Pliable*. Now by this time the man was a good distance ahead of them; however they were resolved to pursue him, and this they did and in a little while overtook him.

Then said the man [*Christian*], "Neighbors, why have you come after me?" They said, "To persuade you to go back with us." But he said, "That can by no means be. You dwell in the *City of Destruction*, (the place where I also was born) as it appears, and dying there sooner or later, you will sink lower than the grave, into a place that burns with fire and brimstone.[2] Be more content good neighbors, and go along with me."

OBSTINATE: What! And leave our friends and our comforts behind us!

CHRISTIAN: Yes (now claiming the pilgrim name of *Christian*),[3] because all of that which you cling to, and should forsake, is not worthy to be compared with a little of that which I am seeking to enjoy;[4] and if you will go along with me and persevere, you shall obtain even as I myself; for where I go there is more than enough to spare.[5] So come away with me and prove my words.

---

1 They that fly from the wrath to come are a gazing-stock [*entertaining spectacle*] to the world. Jer. 20:10.

2 *Gen. 19:24; Rev. 20:15; 21:8.*

3 *The pilgrim claims to be a Christian before entering the Wicket-gate.*

4 *Rom. 8:18*; II Cor. 4:18.

5 Luke 15:17, that is enough grace and mercy.

OBSTINATE: What are the things that you seek, since you leave all of the world to find them?

CHRISTIAN: I seek an inheritance that is incorruptible, undefiled, and does not fade away; and it is laid up in *Heaven*,[6] being secure there,[7] ready to be bestowed at the appointed time upon those that diligently seek it. Read about it, if you will, in my book.

OBSTINATE: Tush [*nonsense*], put away your foolish book. Tell me whether you will return with us or not.

CHRISTIAN: No, not for a moment, because I have laid my hand to the plough [*and will not look back*].[8]

OBSTINATE: Come then, neighbor Pliable, let us turn about and go home without him. He represents those crazy-headed coxcombs [*pompous and silly strutting cocks*] who, when possessed by some blind passion, are wiser in their own eyes than seven men who can offer a reason.[9]

PLIABLE: Perhaps you are right. But don't be so critical; if what good *Christian* says is true, then the things that he seeks after are better than ours; my heart is inclined to go with my neighbor.

OBSTINATE: What! Are there more fools than one? Be ruled by me and go back. Who knows where such a brain-sick fellow will lead you? I insist, go back, go back, and be wise.

CHRISTIAN: [10]Come with me neighbor *Pliable*. There are such things to be had which I spoke of, and many more glories besides. If you do not believe me, then read here in my book; for assuredly the truth of what is expressed in these pages has been fully confirmed by the blood of he who wrote it.[11]

PLIABLE: Well neighbor *Obstinate*, I begin to come to a point [*of decision*]. I intend to go along with this good man, and

---

6 I Pet. 1:4.

7 Heb. 11:16.

8 Luke 9:62.

9 *Prov. 26:16.*

10 Christian and Obstinate in conflict over Pliable's soul.

11 *Luke 22:20*; Heb. *9:17-28*; 13:20-21.

throw in my lot with him. But, my good companion, do you know the way to this desirable place?

CHRISTIAN: I have been directed by a man whose name is *Evangelist*, to hasten toward a little gate that is before us, where we will receive further instruction about the way ahead.

PLIABLE: Come then, my good neighbor, let us be on our way. So both of them went on together.

OBSTINATE: And I will go back to my own place. I will be no companion of such misled, fantastical [*eccentric*] fellows.

Obstinate

3

CHRISTIAN AND PLIABLE CONVERSE ALONG THE WAY

NOW I saw in my dream that when *Obstinate* had turned back, *Christian* and *Pliable* talked as they went ahead over the plain; and thus they entered into earnest conversation.

CHRISTIAN: Now tell me, neighbor *Pliable;* how are you getting along? I am glad you were persuaded to come along with me. Had even *Obstinate* felt what I have sensed concerning the powers and terrors of the world to come that are presently unseen, he would not have so lightly turned his back upon us.

PLIABLE: Then good neighbor *Christian*, since there are only the two of us here, do tell me further of the things that are ahead, what they are like, how they will be enjoyed, and where we are going.

CHRISTIAN: I can better appreciate them with my mind than with my tongue. Nevertheless, since you are eager to know, I will describe them to you from my book.

PLIABLE: And do you believe that the words of your book are certainly true?

CHRISTIAN: Yes, definitely so, for it was written by he who cannot possibly lie.[1]

PLIABLE: Well said; tell me, what things are they?

CHRISTIAN: There is an endless kingdom [*Celestial City*] to be inhabited, and everlasting life to be given to us so that we may inhabit that kingdom forever.[2]

PLIABLE: Again, well said; but tell me still more.

CHRISTIAN: There are crowns of glory to be given to us, and garments[3] that will make us shine like the sun in the firmament of *Heaven*.[4]

---

[1] Tit. 1:2.

[2] Isa. 45:17; John 10:27-29.

[3] Matt. 13; II Tim. 4:8; Rev. 3:4.

[4] *Gen. 1:16.*

PLIABLE: This is excellent. What further details are there?

CHRISTIAN: There will be no more crying or sorrow; for he who is the owner of that place will wipe all tears from our eyes.[5]

PLIABLE: And what company shall we have there?

CHRISTIAN: There we shall be with the seraphim and cherubim,[6] creatures that will dazzle your eyes to look on them. There also you shall meet with the thousands and ten thousands that have traveled ahead of us to that place; none of them are unkind, but rather loving and holy, everyone walking in the sight of *God* and standing in his presence with everlasting acceptance. In a word, there we shall see the elders with their golden crowns;[7] there we shall see the holy virgins with their golden harps.[8] There we shall see men who were, by this present world, cut in pieces, burnt in flames, eaten by beasts, drowned in the sea,[9] because of the love that they maintained for the Lord of the place, all well, and clothed with the garment of immortality.[10]

PLIABLE: The hearing of this is enough to ravish a person's heart. But how shall we be able to enjoy and share in these things?

CHRISTIAN: The Lord, the governor of that country, has recorded in this book[11] that, in essence, if we are truly willing to have them, he will bestow them upon us freely.[12]

PLIABLE: Well, my good companion, I am glad to hear of these things; so come on, let us mend our pace [*travel more rapidly*].

---

[5] Isa. 25:8; Rev. 7:16-17; 21:4.

[6] Isa. 6:2; I Thess. 4:16-17; Rev. 5:11.

[7] Rev. 4:4.

[8] Rev. 14:1-5.

[9] John 12:25.

[10] II Cor. 5:2-5.

[11] Isa. 55:12; John 6:37; 7:37; Rev. 21:6; 22:17.

[12] *Isa. 55:1-7; Rom. 3:24; 5:17; 8:32.*

CHRISTIAN: But I cannot go as fast as I would like on account of this burden that is on my back.[13]

Pliable

Help

[13] *Conviction of sin distinguishes Christian from Pliable.*

4

CHRISTIAN AND PLIABLE CONFRONT THE SLOUGH OF DESPOND

NOW I saw in my dream that just as they had ended this talk, they drew near to a very miry slough [*filthy quagmire*] that was in the middle of the plain. And not watching where they were going, they both suddenly fell into the bog. The name of the *Slough* was *Despond.* Here therefore they wallowed for some time, being shamefully bedaubed with the dirt; and *Christian*, because of the burden that was on his back, began to sink into the mire.[1] Then *Pliable* spoke:

PLIABLE: Ah, neighbor *Christian*, where are you now?

CHRISTIAN: To be sure, I do not know.

PLIABLE: (Offended and angry) Is this the happiness you have told me about as we have traveled? If we have such a halting [*crippling*] disaster at this early stage, then what may we expect from now on till the end of our journey? If I escape out of this with my life, you shall possess the brave country alone for me.[2]

Hence *Pliable*, making several toilsome attempts, eventually struggled out of the mire on that side of the *Slough* which was closest to his own house. So he went back and *Christian* saw him no more.

Therefore *Christian* was left to tumble in the *Slough of Despond* alone. But he still endeavored to struggle to that side of the *Slough* that was further from his own house and closer to the *Wicket-gate.*[3] And this he did, yet he was unable to get out because of the burden that was upon his back.

---

1 *Bunyan describes a similar experience in Grace Abounding, § 82.*

2 It is not enough to be pliable.

3 Christian in trouble still seeks to get further from his own house.

However, I [*Bunyan*] saw in my dream that a man came to him named *Help*,[4] and he asked *Christian*, "What are you doing here?"

CHRISTIAN: Sir, I was advised to go this way by a man named *Evangelist*, and he directed me toward the *Wicket-gate* ahead so that I might escape from the wrath to come. But as I was pressing forward, I fell in here.

HELP: But why did you not look for the steps[5] across the mire?

CHRISTIAN: I was so fearful in my escape that I missed the safe way across the mire and fell in.

HELP: Then give me your hand. So *Christian* stretched out his hand, and *Help*[6] lifted him out of the mire and set him on solid ground; then the pilgrim was exhorted to be on his way toward the *Wicket-gate* ahead.

Then I [*Bunyan*] approached the person who lifted him out and said, "Sir, since the way from the *City of Destruction* to the *Wicket-gate* ahead runs directly through this place, why is it that this plat [*low-lying piece of land*] is not repaired so that travelers might pass through with greater safety?" And he said to me, "This miry *Slough* is peculiar in that it cannot be mended. Being low-lying it attracts a continuous stream of scum and filth that is associated with conviction of sin; for this reason it is called the *Slough of Despond*. As the traveling sinner is awakened about his lost condition, there arise in his soul many fears, doubts, and discouraging perceptions concerning himself; then all of these accumulate and pile up in this place. And so this is the reason for the badness of this ground."

"It is not the pleasure of the *King*[7] that this place should remain in such a bad condition. For this reason His laborers have, according to the direction of *His Majesty's* surveyors, been employed for sixteen [*now over nineteen*] hundred years in

---

4 *Ps. 20:1-2; 70:5.*

5 The promises. *II Pet. 1:4.*

6 Ps. 40:2.

7 Isa. 35:3-4.

attempting to mend this piece of ground. Yes, to the best of my knowledge, this location has swallowed up at least twenty thousand cart-loads, that is millions of wholesome instructions that have, at all seasons, been brought from all regions of the *King's* dominions. And those that know from experience say that there is no better material for making the ground solid here. This being so, it might well have been mended, but it remains the *Slough of Despond* still, and so it shall be when they have done what they can."

"It is true, according to the directive of the *Law-giver*, that a number of reliable and solid steps[8] have been placed through the very middle of the *Slough*. But at such a time as this when so much filth spews forth, as is the case during periods of changeable weather, these steps are hardly visible. And even if they are noticed, yet on account of guilt-induced dizziness, their feet miss the steps. So they are thoroughly bemired, notwithstanding that the steps are there. However, the ground does prove to be good [*firm*] once they enter in at the *Gate*."[9]

Now I [*Bunyan*] saw in my dream that by this time, *Pliable* had arrived back at his house. So his neighbors came to visit him, and some of them called him wise on account of his return to his home; some called him a fool for endangering himself with *Christian's* company. But others mocked his cowardliness, saying, "Surely since you commenced your adventure, I would not have been so fainthearted as to give in for a few difficulties." So *Pliable* sat cringing in their midst. But at last he regained his confidence so that his neighbors then turned their attention toward deriding poor *Christian* behind his back. However, that is enough concerning *Pliable*.

---

[8] The promises of forgiveness and acceptance to life by faith in Christ.

[9] I Sam. 12:23.

5
CHRISTIAN ENCOUNTERS MR. WORLDLY-WISEMAN

NOW as *Christian* was walking all alone, he noticed someone else in the distance on his way across the field coming to meet him. And so it happened that they met just when their paths crossed. The name of this particular gentleman was *Mr. Worldly-Wiseman* who resided in the *Town of Carnal-Policy*, a very large community not far removed from *Christian's* former home *Town*. So this man met *Christian* and acted as if he knew of his coming beforehand; the reason was that pilgrims setting out from the *City of Destruction* were usually the subject of intense gossip that spread to many distant towns. Therefore because *Mr. Worldly-Wiseman* had some inkling of his coming, he was easily able to observe *Christian's* laborious approach, his sighs and groans and the like, and thus engage him in sympathetic conversation.

WORLDLY-WISEMAN: Hello there, my good fellow, and where are you traveling with such a burdened manner?

CHRISTIAN: Yes, it certainly is a burdened manner, and as good a one as any poor creature ever had. As to where I am going, sir, let me tell you. I am on my way toward that distant *Wicket-gate* that is just ahead; for there, I have been told, I will gain entrance into the way that will lead to the removal of my heavy burden.

WORLDLY-WISEMAN: Do you have a wife and children?

CHRISTIAN: Yes, but I am so weighed down with this burden that I cannot enjoy them as much as was formerly the case. In fact, it now seems as if I had no family at all.[1]

WORLDLY-WISEMAN: Then will you listen to me if I give you good advice?

CHRISTIAN: Certainly I will, provided it is good, for I am in great need of wise counsel.

---

[1] I Cor. 7:29.

WORLDLY-WISEMAN: Then I would advise you to get rid of your burden with all possible speed; for you will never have peace of mind until then: nor will you be able to enjoy the benefits of the blessing that *God* has bestowed upon you until such a time.

CHRISTIAN: What you describe is certainly what I am seeking after, namely to be rid of my burden. But I cannot get relief by myself, nor do I know of a man in our country who can lift it off from my shoulders. So for this reason I am heading in this direction, as I told you, so that I may be rid of my burden.

WORLDLY-WISEMAN: Who directed you to go this way so as to be rid of your burden?

CHRISTIAN: A man who appeared to me to be a very great and honorable person; his name, as I remember it, is *Evangelist.*

WORLDLY-WISEMAN: I most certainly beshrew [*condemn*] him for his advice, for there is not a more dangerous and troublesome way ahead in all the world than that into which he has directed you; and you will prove this to be so if you submit to his guidance. Indeed, you appear to have experienced some of this trouble already, for I notice dirt on you that surely comes from the *Slough of Despond.*

Yet that *Slough* is but the beginning of your sorrows, even as other pilgrims experience along the same way. Listen to me, since I am older than you! As you proceed along the way ahead, you are likely to experience wearisomeness, painfulness, hunger, perils, nakedness, sword, lions, dragons, darkness, and in a word, death, and what else? These things are certainly true since they have been confirmed by the testimonies of many pilgrims.[2] So why should a man so carelessly place himself in danger by paying attention to the advice of a stranger?

CHRISTIAN: Why, sir, this burden on my back is more terrible to me than all of those things that you have mentioned. No, to give careful thought, I don't care what I meet with in the way as long as I can eventually be delivered from my burden.[3]

WORLDLY-WISEMAN: How then did you come by your burden in the first place?

---

2 *I Cor. 15:30-32; II Cor. 11:23-27.*

3 The frame of the heart of young Christians.

CHRISTIAN: By reading this book in my hand.

WORLDLY-WISEMAN: I thought so. It has happened to you in the same way that other weak men, in meddling with things that are too high for them,[4] have suddenly fallen into the same bewilderment that you presently suffer. Now this con-fusion not only humiliates men, even as I observe that you have suffered, but it also causes them to pursue desperate causes, and so seek that which they know little about.

CHRISTIAN: Well, I know what I want to obtain, and that is relief from my heavy burden.

WORLDLY-WISEMAN: But why do you seek for ease with regard to your present way seeing that it involves so many dangers? If you had but patience enough to listen to me, I would advise you how to obtain what you desire, only without the perils that you are certain to encounter if you follow the way ahead. Yes, and further, the remedy I would suggest is close at hand. Besides, I will offer yet more, for instead of dangers you will meet with much safety, friendship, and content.

CHRISTIAN: Pray sir, do explain to me this secret.

WORLDLY-WISEMAN: Why a short distance away is the *Village Morality*, in which their lives a gentleman whose name is *Legality*.[5] Now he is a very judicious man of the highest reputation, and as such he is well able to assist men with the removal of burdens from their shoulders such as you have. In fact to my knowledge he has been a great help to many pilgrims in this regard. Yes, and besides this, he is most skillful in curing those who are plagued with anxiety concerning their burdens. To him you should go right now for immediate help. His house is less than a mile from here, and if perhaps you should not find him at home, then he has a very pleasant son named *Civility* who is able to give the same assistance as his father.

As I have said, there you can be relieved of your burden, and should you then prefer not to return home, as I would indeed recommend, you can then send for your wife and children to

---

[4] Mr. Worldly-Wiseman does not like that men should be serious in reading the Bible.

[5] Here Mr. Worldly-Wiseman prefers Morality before the Straight Gate.

come to this *Village*. There you will also find suitable empty houses available that are reasonably priced. Living standards and food, while being inexpensive, are of a very high quality. Added to this enjoyable environment would be the company of honest neighbors who maintain financial security and an attractive lifestyle.

Now *Christian* was somewhat of two minds concerning what he should do. But he soon concluded that if what this congenial gentleman said was true, then his wisest course would be for him to take his advice.[6] So with this in mind, he further spoke with *Mr. Worldly-Wiseman*.

CHRISTIAN: Sir, which way is it that I should take to this honest man's house?

WORLDLY-WISEMAN: Do you see a high hill[7] that is just ahead of you?

CHRISTIAN: Yes, very clearly.

WORLDLY-WISEMAN: Then you must go beyond that *Hill*, and the first house you will come to is that of *Mr. Legality*.

Mr. Worldly-Wiseman

---

6 Christian snared by Mr. Worldly-Wiseman's word.

7 Mount Sinai.

6

CHRISTIAN SEEKS AFTER THE VILLAGE OF MORALITY

SO *Christian* departed from his present course so as to head toward *Mr. Legality's* house for help. But notice that when he had drawn very close to the *Hill*, it seemed so high that it appeared to almost hang over him and threaten to crush him. Being paralyzed with fear, he stopped rather than go any further. As a result he did not know what to do. Also his burden now seemed much heavier than when he was formerly in the way.

There also came flashes of fire erupting out of the *Hill* that made *Christian* fear that he would be burned.[1] For this reason he was terrified and began to sweat and tremble in his body.[2] Now he was sorry [*repented*] that he had taken *Mr. Worldly-Wiseman's* advice. Yet at that very moment he saw *Evangelist* coming directly toward him, and this caused him to blush with shame. So *Evangelist* drew near, while appearing to be most indignant in his mood, for he seemed eager to talk soberly with *Christian*.

EVANGELIST: What are you doing here?[3] (At this *Christian* was at a loss for words. He just stood speechless.) Are you not the same person that I found weeping outside the walls of the *City of Destruction*?

CHRISTIAN: Yes, my dear sir, I am that man.

EVANGELIST: Then how is it that you have so quickly turned aside from my direction, for you are now going the wrong way?[4]

CHRISTIAN: Soon after I left the *Slough of Despond*, I met a very sympathetic gentleman who persuaded me that I could, in

---

1 Ex. 19:16, 18.

2 Heb. 12:21.

3 *I Kgs. 19:9, 13.*

4 *Gal. 1:6.*

the *Village* just ahead, find a man who was able to relieve me of my burden.

EVANGELIST: Who was he?

CHRISTIAN: He appeared to be such a gentleman in both his appearance and conversation. Eventually he got me to yield to his advice, and so I came here. But when I drew close to this *Hill* and discovered how it hangs over the way, I immediately halted lest it should fall on my head.

EVANGELIST: And what did that gentleman say to you?

CHRISTIAN: Why he asked me where I was going, and so I told him.

EVANGELIST: And what did he say to you then?

CHRISTIAN: He asked me if I had a family, and I told him. But I also explained that on account of being so heavily burdened down, I did not have as much pleasure in them as was formerly the case.

EVANGELIST: So what did he then say?

CHRISTIAN: He advised me to be quickly rid of my burden, and at this I explained that I really did want the relief that he recommended. I further told of my traveling toward the *Gate* ahead for the purpose of receiving direction as to how I might reach the *Place of Deliverance.* So he said that he would show me a much better and shorter way, being far less troublesome, sir, than that which you counseled me about.

So he pointed me to another gentleman's house where, he explained, there were men well able to take away burdens such as mine. So I believed him, and departed from the way along this alternative route with the hope that I might soon be eased of my burden. But when I came to this place, and saw things as they really are, I immediately stopped in my tracks out of fear of great danger, as already described. But now I do not know what to do.

EVANGELIST: Then stand still for a little while, so that I can explain to you the *Word of God.*[5] (*Christian* quietly listened and trembled.) Make sure that you do not reject he who speaks to you as was the manner of *Israel*. For if *God's* ancient people

---

[5] *I Sam. 9:27.*

did not escape judgment when they refused to heed *God's* messenger on *Earth*, how much more shall we not escape if we turn away from he who speaks from *Heaven*?[6]

Moreover, the just shall live by faith; but if any man draws back, my soul shall have no pleasure in him.[7] (Then he made specific application.) You are the man who, in running into such a miserable backslidden condition, have begun to reject the counsel of the most high *God* and withdraw your feet from walking along the way of peace, even to the point of being in danger of eternal perdition.[8]

Then *Christian* fell down at his feet as if dead, lamentably crying, "Woe is me, for I am undone [*ruined*]."[9] At the sight of this *Evangelist* caught him by the right hand saying, "All manner of sin and blasphemies shall be forgiven men; be not faithless, but believing."[10] As a consequence *Christian* revived a little more and stood up trembling before *Evangelist*, even as he had first done.

Then *Evangelist* continued to speak, saying, "Give more earnest attention to the things that I shall tell you about. I will now show you who it was that deluded you, and also to whom it was he sent you. The man that met you is none other than *Mr. Worldly-Wiseman*, and how right it is for him to have this name. The reason is partly because he favors only the doctrine of this world,[11] therefore he always attends church in the *Town of Morality*, and partly because he loves the doctrine of that *Town* the best, for it saves him from the *Cross*.[12] So because he is of a carnal nature, therefore he seeks to oppose my ways, even though they are right."

---

6 Heb. 12:25.

7 *Hab. 2:4*; Heb. 10:38.

8 *II Sam. 12:7.*

9 *Isa. 6:5.*

10 Matt. 12:31; Mark 3:28; *John 20:27.*

11 I John 4:5.

12 Gal. 6:12.

"Now there are three things in this man's counsel that you must utterly detest.[13]

1. His ability to lead you out of the way.

2. His zealous effort to portray the *Cross* as abhorrent to you.

3. And his directing of your feet toward that way which leads to the administration of death."[14]

"First, you must despise his ability to turn you out of the way; yes, and your own agreement to such a proposal as well: because this is to reject the counsel of *God* for the sake of the counsel of a *Worldly-Wiseman.* The *Lord* says, 'Strive to enter in at the strait [narrow] gate,'[15] the gate to which I am sending you; 'for strait is the gate that leads to life, and there are few that find it.'[16] This wicked man has turned you from the *Wicket-gate* and the way that leads up to it, and almost brought you to destruction. Therefore hate his ability to turn you out of the way, and loathe yourself for listening to him."

"Second, you must abhor his zeal in attempting to depict the *Cross* to you as offensive; for you are to prefer it to the treasures of *Egypt*;[17] besides, the *King* of glory has told you that he who will save his life shall lose it;[18] and he who follows *Him*, but does not hate his father and mother, and wife, and children, and brothers, and sisters, yes even his own life as well, cannot be *His* disciple.[19] Therefore I say, for a man to work hard to persuade you that the *King's* advice will lead to your death, yet without any support from the truth, is to be detoured from the way that points you to eternal life. So you must completely loathe this doctrine."

---

[13] Evangelist reveals the deceit of Mr. Worldly-Wiseman. *Heb. 2:1.*

[14] *II Cor. 3:7-11.*

[15] Luke 13:24.

[16] Matt. 7:13-14.

[17] Heb. 11:25-26.

[18] Matt. 10:39; Mark 8:34; John 13:25.

[19] Luke 14:26.

"Third, you must hate his directing of your feet along the way that leads to the ministration of death. And in this respect you must carefully consider the person to whom he sent you, and especially how unable that person is to deliver you from your burden. He to whom you were sent for ease, that is *Legality* by name, is the son of the *Bondwoman* who is in bondage along with her children; she represents *Mount Sinai* as a mystery, which you have feared would fall on your head.[20] Now if she, with her children, are in bondage, then how can you expect to be made free by them? Therefore this *Legality* is not able to set you free from your burden. No man has ever got rid of his burden by him, no, and is not likely to be so delivered in the future."

"You cannot be justified by the works of the law; for no man living can be rid of his burden by means of the works of the law. Therefore *Mr. Worldly-Wiseman* is an alien guide, and *Mr. Legality* a cheat; as for his son *Civility*, in spite of his simpering [*smiling*] manner, he is yet a hypocrite and cannot help you. Believe me, there is no substance in such blustering talk that you have heard from this sottish [*works intoxicated*] man. His only design has been to deprive you of your salvation by means of turning you from the way along which I sent you."[21]

After this *Evangelist* called aloud to the *Heavens* for confirmation of what he had said; and immediately there came words and fire out of the *Mountain*, under which poor *Christian* stood, that made his hair to stand on end. The words that poured forth were as follows: "As many as are of the works of the law are under a curse; for it is written, Cursed is everyone who does not continue to live according to all things that are written in the *Book of the Law*, that is to obey them."[22]

Now *Christian* anticipated nothing but death, and so gave out an agonizing cry, even cursing the occasion when he met *Mr. Worldly-Wiseman*, and called himself a thousand fools for paying attention to his advice. He also felt terribly ashamed to

---

20 *II Cor. 3:7, 9*; Gal. 4:21-27.

21 *II Cor. 11:3.*

22 Gal. 3:10.

think that this gentleman's arguments, though originating from the flesh, should prevail with him and be the cause of his abandonment of the right way. So having scolded himself, he again directed himself to *Evangelist* with great earnestness.

CHRISTIAN: Sir, tell me what you think. Is there any hope for me? May I now return to the right way and then approach the *Wicket-gate*? Or shall I be abandoned on account of my waywardness, and be sent back to certain shame at the *City of Destruction*? I am heartily sorry for having listened to this man's counsel; yet may my sin be forgiven?[23]

EVANGELIST: Your sin is very great since you have in fact committed two evils; you have forsaken the way that is good, and then pursued forbidden paths.[24] Nevertheless, the man at the *Gate* will welcome you because he offers goodwill to approaching pilgrims.[25] Even so, be careful that you do not turn aside again, for then you may perish altogether when his wrath is kindled but a little.[26]

Then *Christian* made preparation to return to the right way. After *Evangelist* had kissed him, encouraged him with a smile, and commended him to *God's* keeping, the pilgrim quickly pressed forward; he was now especially careful not to speak to anyone; even if spoken to by a stranger, he would not offer a reply.[27] Now his manner of walking was as if he was stepping on forbidden ground in unsafe territory; he seemed so intent on reaching the right way where he was first beguiled by the counsel of *Mr. Worldly-Wiseman.*

---

23 Christian enquires if he may yet be happy.

24 *Jer. 2:13.*

25 Evangelist comforts Christian. *Luke 2:14, KJV.*

26 Ps. 2:12.

27 *Luke 10:4.*

7
CHRISTIAN ARRIVES AT THE WICKET-GATE

SO after a while *Christian* arrived at the *Wicket-gate.* Now over the gate there was written, *Knock and it shall be opened unto you.*[1] Therefore he knocked more than once or twice while saying:

> May I now enter here? Will he within
> Open to sorry me, though I have bin [*been*]
> An undeserving rebel? Then shall I
> Not fail to sing his lasting praise on high.

At last their came to the *Gate* a grave [*dignified*] person named *Good-will*, who asked, "Who is there? From where have you come? What is your purpose in knocking?"

CHRISTIAN: Here is a poor burdened sinner who comes from the *City of Destruction.* But more importantly, I am going to *Mount Zion* [*the Celestial City*],[2] so that I may be delivered from the wrath to come. Therefore sir, since I have been informed that the way to my destination is through this *Gate*, I would like to know if you are willing to let me enter.

GOOD-WILL: I am willing with all my heart.[3] (And at that he immediately opened the *Gate.*)

Now as *Christian* was stepping through the *Gate*, he was quite surprised when suddenly, *Good-will* pulled him through.[4] In seeking an explanation for this forceful manner, *Christian* was told, "Just a little distance outside this *Gate,* a strong castle has been built and its captain is named *Beelzebub.*[5] From there, both he and his army shoot arrows at those who seek entrance at

---

[1] Matt. 7:7-8.

[2] *I Chron. 11:4-9; Ps. 2:6; 48:1-2; Heb. 12:22-24.*

[3] The Gate will be opened to broken-hearted sinners. *Ps. 51:17.*

[4] *Jer. 31:3; John 6:44.*

[5] *Matt. 12:24-27.*

the *Gate*, endeavoring to slay pilgrims before they pass through."[6] Then said *Christian*, "I rejoice and tremble."[7] So when the pilgrim was fully inside, *Good-will* asked him, "Who directed you to come this way?"

CHRISTIAN: *Evangelist* exhorted me to come this way and knock at the *Gate*, just as I did. He further told me that you, sir, would tell me what I must do next.

GOOD-WILL: An open door is set before you, and no man can shut it.[8]

CHRISTIAN: Now I begin to reap the benefits of my hazards.

GOOD-WILL: But how is it that you have come alone?

CHRISTIAN: Because none of my neighbors saw their danger as I saw mine.

GOOD-WILL: Did any of them know of your coming?

CHRISTIAN: Yes, my wife and children were the first to notice my departure, and they called out for me to return home. Also some of my neighbors cried out as a group for me to come back. But I put my fingers in my ears and continued on my way.

GOOD-WILL: But did none of them follow you to persuade you to go back?

CHRISTIAN: Yes, both *Obstinate* and *Pliable*. But when they realized that their arguments had not been successful, *Obstinate* turned back in a rage, though *Pliable* did come with me for a short while.

GOOD-WILL: But why did he not persevere even to this place?

CHRISTIAN: Quite frankly, we did press on together, that is until we came to the *Slough of Despond* into which we both suddenly tumbled. At that point, my neighbor *Pliable* was immediately discouraged and refused to go any further. As a result, he drew himself out of the mire on that side which was nearest to his house; he then told me that I would possess the

---

6 Satan envies those who enter the narrow Gate.

7 *Ps. 2:11.*

8 *Rev. 3:8.*

brave country alone on his behalf. So he went back in the direction of *Obstinate* and I proceeded forward to this *Gate.*[9]

GOOD-WILL: How sad it is concerning *Pliable* in that he had such little appreciation of the heavenly glory to come, so much so that he did not consider it worth encountering a few hazards and difficulties to obtain it.

CHRISTIAN: Yes, this account concerning *Pliable* is sadly true. Though the truth with regard to myself is really no different. It is a fact that *Pliable* returned to his own house. But I also carnally yielded to the persuasive arguments of *Mr. Worldly-Wiseman*, and consequently turned aside toward the way that leads to death.[10]

GOOD-WILL: Oh, did he prey upon you as well? Did he beguile you by offering relief and ease by means of *Mr. Legality*? You know they are both cheats. But did you pay attention to his advice?

CHRISTIAN: Yes, I went ahead as far as I dared to find *Mr. Legality*, that is until I feared that the mountain that lies beside his house would fall upon my head. And so for this reason I was forced to stop.

GOOD-WILL: That mountain has been the death of many, and will be the death of many more. It is just as well you escaped lest it dash you to pieces.

CHRISTIAN: Why, to be truthful, I do not know what would have become of me there had not *Evangelist* arrived at just the right time when I was feeling sorry for myself and so miserably depressed. But it was the mercy of *God* that he came to me again, for otherwise I would never have come to this place. Nevertheless, I have come, unworthy as I certainly am, and am more deserving of death by means of that mountain than the privilege of standing before my *Lord* to talk with him. But oh, what a gracious privilege it is for me to gain entrance here.

GOOD-WILL: We do not object to any entering here, notwithstanding all that they have done in the past; in no way

---

9 A pilgrim may have company when he first sets out for Heaven, and yet later find that he travels alone.

10 Christian accuses himself before Good-will.

are they cast out.[11] Therefore my good *Christian*, walk a little distance with me and I will instruct you about the way ahead that you must pursue. Look just ahead of you; do you see this narrow way and how it goes ahead of us? Then that is the way along which you must go. It was established by the patriarchs, prophets, *Christ*, and his apostles; it is as straight a way as it is possible to find. This is the way that you must go.

CHRISTIAN: But are there no turnings or windings or detours by means of which a stranger can lose his way?[12]

GOOD-WILL: Yes, there are many side paths that attach to this narrow way, and they are crooked and wide. But you must distinguish the right way from that which is wrong by observing that it is straight and narrow.[13]

Then I saw in my dream that *Christian* further asked *Good-will* if he was able to help him take off the burden remaining on his back, since it seemed impossible to remove without assistance.[14] *Good-will* advised that he should be content to bear this load until he came to the *Place of Deliverance* further ahead; then the burden would fall from off his back by itself.[15]

So *Christian* began to gird up his loins [*prepare himself*] and seriously pay attention to the journey before him. *Good-will* then told him that when he had traveled some distance from the *Gate*, he would come to the house of the *Interpreter*; having knocked at the door, there he would be shown excellent things.[16] At this, *Christian* said farewell to *Good-will* who in turn bid [*commended to*] him Godspeed [*traveling mercies*].

---

[11] Christian is again comforted. John 6:37.

[12] Christian is afraid of losing his way.

[13] Matt. 7:13-14.

[14] Christian is weary of his burden.

[15] There is no deliverance from the guilt and burden of sin except by the blood and death of Christ.

[16] *The ministry of the Holy Spirit. John 14:26; 15:26; 16:13-14.*

8
CHRISTIAN IS INSTRUCTED AT THE HOUSE OF THE INTERPRETER

THEN he went on till he came to the house of the *Interpreter*, where he knocked at the entrance over and over again. At last someone came to the door and asked, "Who is there?"

CHRISTIAN: Sir, I am a traveler who was advised by an acquaintance of the good man of this house to call here for my benefit. Therefore I would like to speak with the master of this house.

So the man at the door called for the master of the house, who soon came to *Christian* and asked him what was the reason for his visit.

CHRISTIAN: Sir, I am a man who has come from the *City of Destruction* and am on my way to *Mount Zion.* I was told by one *Good-will* at the *Wicket-gate*, the commencement of this narrow way, that if I called here you would show me excellent things that would be of help to me in my journey.

INTERPRETER: By all means come in, and I will certainly show you things that you will find beneficial.[1]

So he commanded his helper to light the candle[2] and then invited *Christian* to follow him.

A. The Portrait of the Godly Pastor

Now *Interpreter* led the pilgrim into a private room, and there he ordered his man to open a door. Then did *Christian* see the picture of a very grave [*serious, important*] person hanging against the wall,[3] and its features were as follows. This man had his eyes directed up toward *Heaven*, the best of books in his hand, the law of truth was written upon his lips, the world was

---

[1] *Matt. 13:10-11; I John 2:20, 27.*

[2] Illumination. *Ps. 119:105.*

[3] Christian sees a picture of bravery [*courage in conflict*].

behind his back; he stood as if he pleaded with men, and a crown of gold hung over his head.[4]

CHRISTIAN: What then does this mean?

INTERPRETER: The man in the picture which you see is one in a thousand, who can beget children,[5] travail in birth with children, and nurse them himself when they are born.[6] And just as you see him with his eyes looking up toward *Heaven*, the best of books in his hand, and the law of truth written on his lips, this is to show you that his work is to know and unfold dark things to sinners.

Similarly, just as you see him stand as if he pleaded with men, and also you notice that the world is cast behind him, and that a crown hangs over his head, this is to show you that, in slighting and despising the things of the present, on account of his love and devotion to his *Master's* service, he is sure to have glory for his reward in the world to come.

Now I have showed you this picture first, because the man who it portrays is the only man who the *Lord* of the *Celestial City* has authorized to be your guide in all of the difficult situations that you may encounter along the way. Therefore pay attention to what I have showed you, and carefully weigh in your mind what you have seen lest, in your journey, you meet with some that pretend to lead you along the right path, while in reality their way leads to death.[7]

B. The Distinction Between the Law and the Gospel

Then *Christian* was taken by the hand and led into a very large parlor [*living room*] that was full of dust having never been swept. Now after he had observed this scene for a little while, *Interpreter* called for a man to commence sweeping. As a result, the dust began to fly about so overwhelmingly that *Christian* was nearly choked to death. *Interpreter* immediately spoke to a gracious lady standing nearby, "Bring some water here and

---

4 *Mal. 2:4-7.*

5 I Cor. 4:15.

6 Gal. 4:19; I Thess. 2:7.

7 *Prov. 14:12.*

sprinkle this room." The lady having done this, the parlor was then easily swept and cleansed.

CHRISTIAN: What does this mean?

INTERPRETER: This parlor is the heart of a man who has never been sanctified [*regenerated and justified*] by the sweet grace of the *Gospel*. The dust is his original [*Adamic*] sin and inward corruptions that have thoroughly defiled the whole man. He who first began to sweep is the *Law*; but the gracious lady who brought water and sprinkled the room is the *Gospel*.[8]

Now while you saw, as soon as the man began to sweep, that the dust so swirled about the room that it became even more difficult to cleanse, and you were near choked to death, this is to show you that the *Law*, instead of it effectively cleansing the heart from sin, does in fact arouse, give greater strength to, and cause sin to flourish in the soul.[9] And this result is in spite of the fact that the *Law* both uncovers and condemns sin, for it does not have the power to subdue.

Furthermore, as you saw the gracious lady sprinkle the room with water, at which it was very easily cleansed, this is to show you that when the *Gospel* comes with its sweet and precious influences indwelling the heart, then, just as you saw the lady settle the dust by sprinkling the floor with water, so is sin vanquished and subdued, and the heart made clean, through the faith of that soul; and consequently that same soul is then made a suitable place for the *King of Glory* to inhabit.[10]

C. The Virtue of Patience Contrasted with Passion

Moreover, I saw in my dream that *Interpreter* again took *Christian* by the hand and led him into a very small room in which there sat two little children, each one on his chair. The name of the elder was *Passion* and the other *Patience*.[11] *Passion* seemed to be very discontented while *Patience* remained calm and quiet. Then *Christian* asked, "What is the reason for

---

[8] *Ezek. 36:25-27.*

[9] Rom. 5:20; 7:6; I Cor. 15:56; *Gal. 3:19.*

[10] John 15:3, 13; Acts 15:9; Rom. 16:25-26; Eph. 5:26.

[11] *Acts 14:15; Jas. 5:8.*

Passion's unrest?" *Interpreter* replied, "The *Governor* of these children would have him wait for the best things that are to be bestowed at the beginning of the next year. But he wants to have his inheritance now, while *Patience* is quite willing to wait."

Then I saw a person come to *Passion* and bring him a bag of treasure that was immediately poured out at his feet. At this the elder child rejoiced and at the same time scornfully laughed at *Patience*. However, I noticed that very soon *Passion's* wealth wasted away, with the result that he found himself left with nothing but rags.

CHRISTIAN: Explain this matter to me more fully.

INTERPRETER: These two lads are figures [*portrayals*] of the men of this world. Now *Patience* represents those men who are prepared to wait for that which is to come. On the other hand you will notice that *Passion* must have all of his inheritance now, this very year, that is in this present world. So are the men of this world: they insist on having all of their good things now and cannot possibly wait till next year, that is in the world to come, for lasting treasure. That proverb, "A bird in the hand is worth two in the bush", is of more authority with them than all of the *Divine Testimonies* [*Scripture accounts*] of the good things promised in the world to come. But as you saw, *Passion* quickly wasted away all that he had so that he ended up having nothing but rags. And so it will be with all like men at the end of this age.

CHRISTIAN: Now I see that *Patience* has superior wisdom, and that for several reasons. 1. Because he is willing to wait for the best things. 2. And also because the glory of his inheritance will last when that of *Passion* has long ago been reduced to rags.

INTERPRETER: Yes, and you may add another reason as well. It is that the glory of the next world will never wear out while the good things of the present decay and then suddenly are gone. Therefore *Passion* did not have a very good reason for laughing at *Patience* even if he did have his good things first; the reality is that *Patience* will have the last laugh because he eventually receives the best things that last eternally. For he who is first must yield to he who was last, because the last must have his time in the future, while the first must make way for nothing because his good things vanish![12]

Therefore he who has his inheritance first, uses and spends it in time; but he who receives his portion last, has it for all of eternity! Therefore it is said of *Dives* [*the rich man*], "In your life you received the good things, and likewise *Lazarus* [*the beggar*] received evil things; but now he is comforted and you are tormented."[13]

CHRISTIAN: Then I understand that it is not good to covet things that are now, but to wait for the best things that are to come.

INTERPRETER: You certainly speak the truth. For the things that are seen are temporal; but the things that are not seen are eternal.[14] However, though this be so, yet since present things and our fleshly desires are such close neighbors, one next to the other; and again, because things to come and our carnal appetite are such strangers [*so opposed*] to one another: therefore it is that the first of these [*present things and fleshly desires*] so quickly establish friendship, and that distance is maintained between the second [*eternal things*].[15]

D. The Grace of Christ Conquers the Assailed Heart

Then I saw in my dream that the *Interpreter* took *Christian* by the hand, and led him to a place where there was a fire burning against a wall. In front of this fireplace was a man continually casting buckets of water on the fire in an effort to extinguish it. Nevertheless, the fire continued to burn higher and hotter.

CHRISTIAN: What does this mean?

INTERPRETER: This fire is the work of grace that has been ignited in the heart. He who casts water upon it, so as to extinguish this blaze, is the *Devil*.[16] Even so, in that you see the

---

[12] *Matt. 20:16.*

[13] Luke 16:25.

[14] II Cor. 4:18.

[15] *Gal. 5:16-17.*

[16] *Bunyan describes this experience in Grace Abounding, § 110.*

fire burn higher and hotter, let me now show you the reason for this mystery.

So *Interpreter* took *Christian* behind the wall and the fireplace; there the pilgrim saw a *Man* with a container in his hand, from which he cast oil upon the fire, though secretly.[17]

Then said *Christian*, "What does this mean?" Hence *Interpreter* replied, "This is *Christ*, who continually, with the oil of his grace, maintains the work already begun in the heart; by this means, notwithstanding what the *Devil* attempts to do, the souls of his people still prove to be gracious.[18] And in that you saw that the *Man* stood behind the wall to maintain the fire, this is to teach you that it is hard for those who are tempted to understand how this work of grace is upheld in the soul."

E. The Persevering Valiant Pilgrim

I also saw that the *Interpreter* took him again by the hand, and led *Christian* into a very pleasant place where a stately palace had been built; it was a very beautiful building indeed. Now the pilgrim was greatly delighted at what he saw, and particularly with the sight of several people, clothed in gold, walking around the top of the palace. Then said *Christian*, "May we go inside?"

Then the *Interpreter* led him closer to the main door, and there he noticed a large number of men who obviously desired to gain entrance, yet seemed to lack courage. Back a little from the door there was also a man sitting at a table with a book and inkhorn [*ink container, used with a quill*] in front of him; his role was that of recording the names of those who were determined to enter the palace.[19] But *Christian* also saw that in the very doorway there stood many armored men who were intent on employing violence and mischief to stop any man from gaining entrance. At this the eager pilgrim pondered what all this meant.

Then, while most of the men outside cowered at the thought of attempting to make a forceful entrance, *Christian* noticed one

---

17 *Zech. 4:11-14.*

18 II Cor. 12:9.

19 *Ezek. 9:1-11.*

man, very resolute in appearance, stride up to the man at the desk and ask of him, "Sir, set down my name." Immediately following this, the same man drew his sword, put a helmet on his head, and rushed toward the palace door with the men standing in the way. So the valiant entrant found himself opposed with deadly force; yet he was not discouraged, and consequently applied himself to fierce cutting and hacking of his opponents. He both received and gave many wounds to his enemies;[20] nevertheless this courageous man cut his way through so that he eventually gained entrance into the palace.

Then those inside, and especially three at the top, cried out with a joyous chorus of welcome,

Come in, come in,
Eternal Glory you shall win.

So he went in and was clothed with garments similar to those being worn by the citizens of the palace. Then *Christian* smiled and said, "I certainly know the meaning of this."

F. The Despairing Reprobate in the Iron Cage

Then *Christian* said, "Now let me go forward." But the *Interpreter* replied, "No, you must stay until I have showed you a little more. After this you can be on your way." So he took him by the hand again and led him into a very dark room where a man sat in an iron cage.[21] Now this man seemed very sad to look upon. He sat with his eyes looking down toward the ground, his hands tightly folded together; and he sighed as if his heart would break. Then said *Christian*, "What does this mean?" So the *Interpreter* told him to talk with the man.

CHRISTIAN: What are you doing here?

MAN: I am what I once was not.

CHRISTIAN: What were you once?

MAN: I was once a fair [*attractive*], flourishing [*thriving*] and professing Christian,[22] in the eyes of both myself and others. At one time I was convinced of being fair [*well set*] for reaching the

---

20 *Matt. 11:12;* Acts 14:22.

21 Despair is like an iron cage.

22 Luke 8:13.

Celestial City; and even had joyous thoughts of arrival at that destination.

CHRISTIAN: Yes, but what are you now?

MAN: I am now a man of despair and am shut up [*captive*] to it, as this iron cage depicts. I cannot get out. Oh how miserable I am since now I cannot get out.

CHRISTIAN: But how did you come to be in this condition?

MAN: I neglected to watch and be sober; I loosed any restraint that had been on my lusts and gave them free reign; I sinned against the light of the *Word* and the goodness of *God*; I have grieved the *Holy Spirit* so that He has departed from me;[23] I have provoked *God* to anger and He has abandoned me; I have so hardened my heart that I cannot repent.

Then *Christian* spoke to the *Interpreter*, "But is there no hope for such a man as this?" "You ask him," replied the *Interpreter*.

CHRISTIAN: Do you have any hope that you will not be permanently kept in this iron cage of despair?

MAN: No, none at all.

CHRISTIAN: But why ought that to be so? Are you not aware that the *Son of the Blessed* is very merciful and compassionate?[24]

MAN: Nevertheless I have crucified him again by my life; I have despised his person;[25] I have despised his righteousness; I have regarded his blood as something quite unholy; I have done despite to [*spitefully opposed, insulted*] the *Spirit* of grace.[26] Therefore I have shut myself out of all of the promises of *God*; and there now remains for me nothing but threatenings, fearful prospects of rebuke, fiery indignation, and certain judgment that shall, as would some adversary, wholly consume me.

CHRISTIAN: For what reasons did you bring yourself into this sorry condition?

MAN: On account of the lusts, pleasures, and profits of this world. It was in the enjoyment of these things that I promised

---

23 *Eph. 4:30.*

24 *Jas. 5:11.*

25 Luke 19:14.

26 Heb. 6:4-6; 10:28-29.

myself increasing delight. But now they all, as it were, snap back and bite me; they gnaw at my soul like a burning worm.[27]

CHRISTIAN: But can you not now repent and turn from this wretched condition?

MAN: [*No*], for *God* has denied me repentance; His *Word* gives me no encouragement to believe. Yes, He himself has shut me up in this iron cage so that even all the men in the world are unable to obtain my release. Oh eternity! eternity! How can I possibly grapple with the misery that I shall encounter in eternity?

INTERPRETER: So remember this man's misery, and let his sorry condition be a perpetual warning to you.

CHRISTIAN: Well, this is a most fearful situation. May *God* help me to watch and be sober, and pray that I may shun the cause of this man's grief. But sir, is it not now time for me to be on my way?

INTERPRETER: Wait just a little longer so that I can show you one more thing, and then you can continue with your journey.

G. The Warning of the Final Day of Judgment

So once again he took *Christian* by the hand and led him into a chamber [*bedroom*] where he observed a man getting out of his bed; and as he put on his clothing he shook and trembled. Then said *Christian*, "Why does this man tremble so much?" *Interpreter* then asked the man to explain the reason for his shaking.

So he began and said, "This evening I was fast asleep, and at the same time I dreamed, and behold the heavens became extremely black; also the sky was laced with lightening and thunder in a manner that was terribly frightening, so much so that I was greatly distressed. Then I looked up in my dream and saw the clouds roll across the sky at an unusually swift rate, at which I heard the great sound of a trumpet and also saw a *Man* sit upon a cloud attended with thousands of heavenly beings;

[27] *Mark 9:48.*

and they were all in the midst of flaming fire, even as the heavens were blazing with fire."[28]

"Then I heard a voice calling, 'Arise you who are dead, and come to your judgment!' And at this the rocks shattered into pieces, the graves opened, and the dead that were in them came forth; some of them were exceedingly glad and joyously looked upward; and some sought to hide themselves under the mountains."[29]

"Then I saw the *Man* that sat upon the cloud open the *Book*, and he commanded the world to draw near. Now on account of the fiery flame that came from his person and surrounded him,[30] there was a necessary distance between he and those called into his presence. Similarly, in just the same way there is a necessary space between a judge and prisoners at the bar in this world. I also heard that those who attended the *Man* who sat on the cloud were ordered, 'Gather together the tares, the chaff, and stubble, and cast them into the burning lake.'"[31]

"At this the *Bottomless Pit* immediately opened up, and I would add, very near where I stood; out of that yawning mouth there spewed forth great billows of smoke and coals of fire, along with hideous noises.[32] To the same attendants it was also commanded, 'Gather my wheat into my garner [*storehouse*].'[33] And with that I saw many caught up and carried away into the clouds, but I was left behind.[34] So I also sought to hide myself, but could not, for the *Man* who sat upon the cloud continuously kept his eye on me: further, my sins all came to mind and my

---

28 Ps. 5:1-3; Isa. 26:21; Dan. 7:10; Mic. 7:16-17; *Matt. 26:64;* John 5:28; I Cor. 15:51-58; I Thess. 4:16; II Thess. 1:7-10; Jude 15; Rev. 20:11-14.

29 *Ps. 50:1-3; Isa. 26:20-21; Matt. 27:50-53; Rev. 6:12-17.*

30 Dan. 7:9-10; Mal. 3:2-3.

31 Mal. 4:1; Matt. 3:2; 13:30.

32 *Rev. 9:1-2, 11; 11:7; 17:8; 20:1-3.*

33 Luke 3:17; I Thess. 4:16-17.

34 *I Thess. 4:13-18.*

conscience accused me from every direction.[35] At this point I then awoke from my sleep."

CHRISTIAN: But what was it that made you so afraid of this sight?

MAN: Why, I thought that the day of judgment had come and that I was not ready for it. But this frightened me the most, that the angels gathered up several standing near me while I was left behind; also the pit of *Hell* opened its mouth near where I was standing. Furthermore, my conscience was in an agony on account of the *Judge* keeping his eyes focused on me with a look of angry disapproval.

Then said the *Interpreter* to *Christian*, "Have you carefully considered all of these things?"

CHRISTIAN: Yes, and they confront me with both hope and fear.[36]

INTERPRETER: Well, keep all of these things at the forefront of your mind so that they can goad you and arouse you to move forward in the right direction.[37] Then *Christian* began to gird up his loins [*make serious preparation*] for moving ahead on his journey. Then said the *Interpreter*, "I pray that the *Comforter* will always be with you,[38] good *Christian*, to guide you in the way that leads to the *Celestial City.*"

So *Christian* went on his way saying,

> Here I have seen things rare, and profitable;
> Things pleasant, dreadful, things to make me stable
> In what I have begun to take in hand:
> Then let me think on them, and understand
> For what purpose they appeared, and let me be
> Thankful, O good *Interpreter*, to thee.

---

[35] Rom. 2:14-15.

[36] *Ps. 2:11.*

[37] *Eccles. 12:11.*

[38] *The Holy Spirit. John 14:16-17.*

9

CHRISTIAN ARRIVES AT THE PLACE OF DELIVERANCE

NOW I saw in my dream that the highway along which *Christian* was to proceed was fenced in on both sides with a *Wall*, and that *Wall* was called *Salvation*.[1] Therefore burdened *Christian* ran up this way, though not without great difficulty, because of the load on his back.

So he ran in this direction until he came to a place where the way ascended up a small hill; and at the top stood a *Cross* while below it was a sepulcher [*stone tomb*]. So I saw in my dream that just as *Christian* came up to the *Cross*, his burden fell from off his back; then it continued to tumble down the hill until it fell into the mouth of the sepulcher and was seen no more.

At this, *Christian* felt glad and overjoyed,[2] and in his excitement he exclaimed, "He has given me rest by means of his sorrow, and life by means of his death." Then he stood still for a while to look with wonder and amazement; for it was so surprising to him that the sight of the *Cross* should accomplish the release of his burden. Therefore he looked again and again, even until inward springs of water flowed down his cheeks.[3] Now as he stood looking and weeping, behold three *Shining Ones* [*angels*] approached and saluted him with the benediction, "Let peace be upon you."[4]

So the first *Shining One* said to him, "Your sins have been forgiven."[5] The second stripped *Christian* of his rags and clothed him with a complete change of garment.[6] The third also set a

---

1 Isa. 26:1; *35:8*.

2 When God releases us from the burden of our guilt, we are as those who leap for joy.

3 Zech. 12:10; *John 4:14; 7:38-39*.

4 *John 20:19, 21, 26*.

5 Mark 2:5.

6 *Isa. 61:10*; Zech. 3:4-5; *Phil. 3:9*.

mark upon his forehead,[7] and gave him a *scroll* with a seal on it,[8] which he directed should be looked at as he ran and handed in upon arrival at the gate of the *Celestial City*. So these messengers went their way. Then *Christian* gave three leaps for joy, and went on singing:[9]

> Thus far did I come laden with my sin,
> Nor could anyone ease the grief that I was in,
> Until I came here. What a place is this!
> Must here be the beginning of my bliss?
> Must here the burden fall from off my back?
> Must here the cords that bound it to me crack?
> Blessed *Cross*! Blessed sepulcher! Blessed rather be
> The *Man* that there was put to shame for me.

The three Shining Ones

---

7 *Ezek. 9:1-7; Rev. 9:1-6; 22:4.*

8 Eph. 1:13.

9 Christian can sing even when alone because God has given to him the joy of his heart.

10

CHRISTIAN OVERTAKES SIMPLE, SLOTH, AND PRESUMPTION

I SAW then in my dream that *Christian* went on his way, that is until he came to the bottom of the hill. There he saw, beside the way, three men fast asleep with chains attached to their heels. The name of one was *Simple*, another was *Sloth*, and the third was *Presumption*.

Upon *Christian* seeing these pilgrims dozing on the ground, he approached them with the hope that he might be able to awaken them. So he exhorted them, "You are like those who fall asleep at the top of a mast, for the *Dead Sea* is under you, that is a gulf that has no bottom.[1] Therefore arouse yourselves and be on the move; if you are willing, I will also help you to be relieved of your shackles." He also told them, "If he who prowls about like a roaring lion should come by, you will certainly become prey for his teeth."[2]

To this they merely glanced at him and replied in the following unconcerned manner: *Simple* naïvely answered, "I do not see any danger." *Sloth* mumbled, "Just let me have a little more sleep." And *Presumption* proudly asserted, "Every tub must stand upon its own bottom [*without the need of assistance*], so what else need I say?"[3] And so they all lay down to sleep again, while *Christian* decided it would be better to be on his way.

Even so, *Christian* was troubled to think that men, in such obvious danger, should so lightly regard the kindness of he who freely offered them assistance, that is by volunteering to help them be relieved of their shackles.

---

[1] Prov. 23:34.

[2] I Pet. 5:8.

[3] If God does not open the eyes of the soul, there will be no persuasion of the truth.

11

CHRISTIAN CONVERSES WITH FORMALIST AND HYPOCRISY

NOW as *Christian* reflected on this disturbing encounter, he noticed two men come tumbling over the *Wall* on the left-hand side of the narrow way; and they hurried along to catch up with him. The name of one was *Formalist*, and the name of the other *Hypocrisy*. So, as I mentioned, they drew near and *Christian* commenced a conversation with them.

CHRISTIAN: Gentlemen, from where have you come, and what is your destination?

FORMALIST AND HYPOCRISY: We were born in the land of *Vain-glory* and are going to *Mount Zion* for the purpose of receiving praise.

CHRISTIAN: Then why did you not enter at the *Wicket-gate* which is located at the beginning of this way? Don't you know that it has been written, "He who does not enter in by the door, but climbs up some other way, that same person is a thief and a robber?"[1]

FORMALIST AND HYPOCRISY: That may be so; however our countrymen have all agreed that this entrance or *Wicket-gate* you mention is too far away. Rather they prefer to take a short cut and climb over the *Wall* at this point, just as we have done.

CHRISTIAN: But will not your custom be regarded as a trespass against the *Lord* of the *Celestial City* to which we are headed, and thus a violation of his revealed will?

FORMALIST AND HYPOCRISY: Well, don't you trouble yourself about that. The reason is that their manner of entry has become a long established custom; in fact many witnesses would testify that it has been accepted as an established route for over a thousand years.[2]

---

1 John 10:1.

2 Those who do not enter the way by the Wicket-gate yet think that they can vindicate their practice of illegitimate entry.

CHRISTIAN: Nevertheless, will your practice stand up to investigation in a court of law?

FORMALIST AND HYPOCRISY: We believe so. Our tradition has been accepted for so long, that is for well over a thousand years, that it would doubtless be admitted as a legal ordinance by any impartial judge. However, practically speaking, we are now in the way; so what does it matter how we got in? If we are in, then we are in. As we understand it, you are in the way having entered through the *Wicket-gate*; and we also are in the way by means of tumbling over the *Wall*. So how is your present condition any different from ours?

CHRISTIAN: I walk by the rule of my *Master*. You walk according to the uninformed working of your imagination. You are already considered to be thieves by the *Lord* of the way. Therefore, I have little doubt that you will be found to be illegitimate pilgrims at the end of the way. You entered in by your own devising without his direction; and so you will leave by yourselves without his mercy. At this they hardly offered a reply, except that they suggested that *Christian* should pay attention to himself. Then I saw each man move ahead, though without much conversation taking place between them. However, the two intruders did have this to say. As to laws and ordinances, doubtless they were as conscientious in obeying them as he. So they continued, "We do not see where you differ from us in the slightest, except for the coat which you are wearing; most likely it was provided by your neighbors to hide your shameful nakedness."

CHRISTIAN: By obedience to laws and ordinances you will not be saved since you did not enter in at the *Wicket-gate*.[3] And as for this coat that I wear, it was given to me by the *Lord* of the *Celestial City* to which I am going. Yes, it is for the purpose of covering my nakedness, and furthermore, I accept it as a token of his kindness granted to me when I earlier wore nothing but rags.[4] Besides, this garment comforts me as I travel. I muse about that time when I shall eventually arrive at the gate of the *Celestial City*; surely the *Lord* will recognize me on account of

---

[3] Gal. 2:16; *Eph. 2:15.*

[4] *Isa. 61:10; Gal. 3:27.*

my wearing his coat, that which he freely gave me on the day when he stripped me of my rags.

Moreover, I have a mark on my forehead which you may not have noticed; it was placed on me by one of my *Lord's* most intimate associates on the same day when my burden fell from off my shoulders. In addition to this I have been given a sealed *scroll* to be read for comfort as I continue along the way; I have been ordered to hand it in at the gate of the *Celestial City* as a token of my authorization to enter. However, I doubt if you desire any of these things, though you do lack them because you did not enter in at the *Wicket-gate*.

To these comments they did not make a reply, except that they looked at each other and then burst out laughing. Then I noticed that they all continued to press forward, though *Christian* moved ahead of them on his own; so not talking with these strangers any longer, he could only muse with himself, sometimes groaning and at other times expressing contentment. For further refreshment he would often read from the *scroll* earlier given to him by one of the *Shining Ones*.

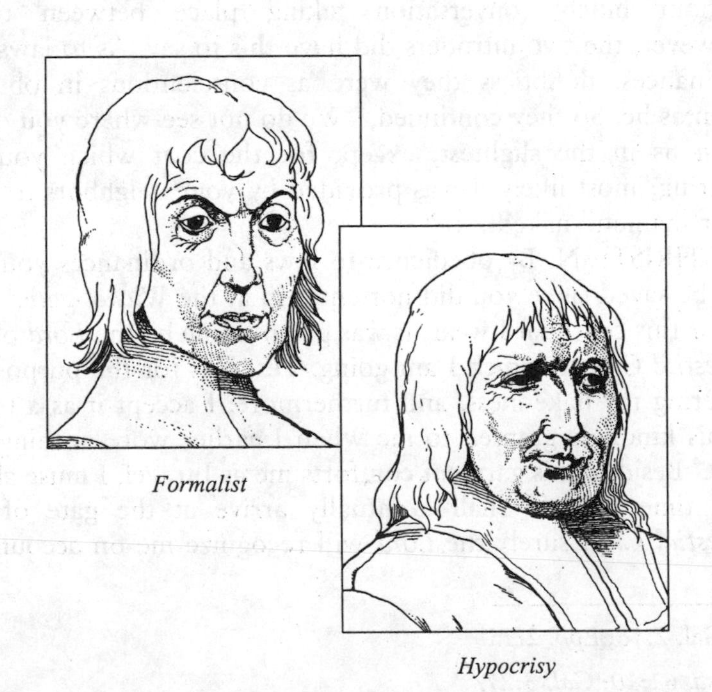

Formalist

Hypocrisy

12

CHRISTIAN ASCENDS THE HILL DICCICULTY

NOW I understand that they all continued on till they came to the foot of a *Hill*, at the bottom of which was a spring. At this same place two other ways joined with the straight way coming from the *Wicket-gate*; one turned to the left hand and the other to the right at the bottom of the *Hill*. However, the narrow way continued straight up the *Hill*, its name being *Difficulty*.

So *Christian* first drank at the spring for refreshment,[1] and then commenced to climb up the *Hill*, saying:

> This *Hill*, though high, I covet to ascend,
> The difficulty will not me offend:
> For I perceive the way to life lies here;
> Come, pluck up, heart; lets neither faint nor fear:
> Better, though difficult, the right way to go,
> Than wrong, though easy, where the end is woe.

Thus *Formalist* and *Hypocrisy* also came to the foot of the *Hill*. Here they saw that it was steep and high, and that there were two alternative ways for them to go along which, they imagined, would later join in with the way of *Christian* beyond the *Hill*. So they decided to follow what appeared to them to be the easier routes;[2] the name of one was *Danger*, and the name of the other *Destruction*. So one proceeded along *Danger* which led him into a great wood; the other went along *Destruction* which entered a wide field full of dark mountains, and there he stumbled and fell never to rise again.[3]

Then I looked toward *Christian* to see just how far he had climbed up the *Hill*. It appeared that he had been reduced from running to walking, and from walking to clambering on his hands and knees because of the steepness of the incline. Now about halfway up the *Hill* was a pleasant *Arbor* [*Shady Resting-*

---

1 *Ps. 110:7*; Isa. 49:10-11.

2 *Prov. 14:12.*

3 *Jer. 13:16.*

place][4] provided by the *Lord* of the *Hill* for the refreshment of weary travelers.

So *Christian* reached this shelter where he then sat down to rest awhile. Then he pulled his *scroll* out of his chest pocket and began to read it for comfort; he also took a fresh look at his new garment which was given to him as he stood before the *Cross*. Thus being pleasantly stimulated for a time, he at first snoozed and then fell fast asleep; as a result, he was detained at that place until near sunset while at the same time his *scroll* fell out of his hand.[5] Now as he was sleeping, someone approached and awakened him with a call, "Go to the ant, you sluggard [*loafer*], and consider her ways, and be wise."[6] At this, *Christian* arose with a jolt and started on his way, racing ahead until he came to the top of the *Hill*.

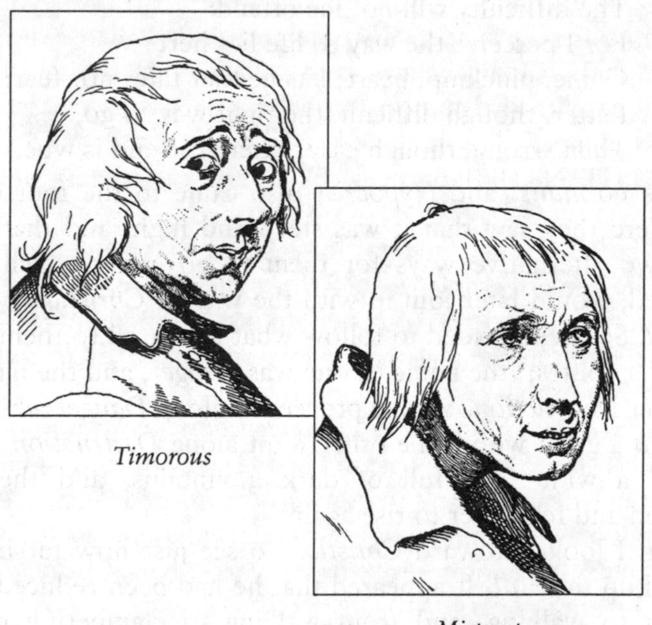

Timorous

Mistrust

---

4 A ward [*place of protection*] of grace.

5 He who sleeps is a loser.

6 Prov. 6:6.

13

CHRISTIAN IS APPROACHED BY TIMOROUS AND MISTRUST

NOW when *Christian* arrived at the top of the *Hill*, two men came running toward him in full flight from the opposite direction. The name of one was *Timorous*, and the name of the other *Mistrust*.[1] To these *Christian* enquired, "Sirs, what is the matter since you are both running the wrong way?" Hence *Timorous* replied "We were making our pilgrimage toward the *City of Zion* and had reached beyond this *Hill Difficulty*; but then the further we went the more danger we encountered. As a result we decided to turn about and return home; so we are now fast on our way."

Then *Mistrust* added, "Yes, this is true, for just ahead of you lying directly in the way is a couple of lions. We were not sure if they were awake or asleep; nevertheless the prospect of our being torn in pieces seemed too real."

CHRISTIAN: You make me afraid, on the other hand where else shall I run to for safety? If I return to my home in the *City of Destruction*, which region is destined for the judgment of fire and brimstone, then I will certainly perish. However, if I can eventually reach the *Celestial City*, then my safety is assured there. Therefore I must press forward, in spite of risks and perils.[2] To go back is to certainly suffer death; but to go forward, though fear of death will threaten along the way, is yet to have the prospect of everlasting life beyond. So I will definitely go forward.

So *Mistrust* and *Timorous* ran down the *Hill*, while *Christian* went on ahead. Even so, in remembering what he had just heard from these men, he felt for his *scroll* in his chest pocket so that he might read it and be comforted. But to his great surprise, the *scroll* was not to be found. As a result *Christian* became very distressed, and did not know what to do; this token was his

---

1 *II Tim. 1:15.*

2 Christian shakes off fear.

means of gaining relief from his fears, as well as being his pass for entering into the *Celestial City*. Therefore at this point the pilgrim was perplexed in not knowing what he should do.

Then he recalled his sleeping at the *Arbor* [*Shady Resting-place*] halfway up the *Hill Difficulty* and suspected what had happened. So falling down on his knees, he asked *God* for forgiveness due to his foolish neglect, and commenced to return down the *Hill* looking for his *scroll*. But oh, who could imagine just how sorrowful of heart he was every step of the way? Sometimes he sighed, and sometimes he wept, and often he rebuked himself for his being so foolish as to sleep at length at that place which had only been erected for the purpose of modest refreshment from weariness.

Therefore he went back, further and further, carefully looking on this side and on that, ever so eager to find that *scroll* which had so often given him comfort on his journey. Thus *Christian* continued downhill until the *Shady Resting-place*, where he had earlier sat and slept, came into view. At this sight his sorrow increased with the more vivid remembrance of his wicked indulgence.[3]

So he continued on bemoaning his sinful sleep and lamenting, "Oh wretched man that I am, that I should sleep in the daytime! that I should sleep in the midst of difficulty! that I should so indulge the flesh as to allow rest, which the *Lord* of the *Hill* has provided only for the relief of pilgrim spirits, and thus give place to carnal ease.[4] Now I have needlessly taken these recent steps, even as *Israel* in the same manner was required to wander and return again by way of the *Red Sea*, on account of their sin. So I am made to tread this way again with sorrow, which ought to have been trodden only with delight, had it not been for this sinful sleep. How far ahead on my way might I have been by this time! Instead, I must tread these steps three times instead of once. Further, now the night is about to overtake me since the day is almost spent. Oh that I had not slept!"

Now by this time he had come to the *Shady Resting-place* once again, where he sat down for a time and wept. But at last,

---

[3] Christian bemoans his foolish sleeping. Rev. 2:4-5.

[4] *Rom. 7:24*; I Thess. 5:7-8.

as *Christian* would have it, while remaining downcast and looking under the seat, there he caught sight of his *scroll*. Now trembling with excitement, he immediately seized it and thrust it into his chest pocket.

And who can possibly tell just how joyful this man was when he had recovered his *scroll*? For this *scroll* was the assurance of his life, and the token of his acceptance at the desired haven. Therefore *Christian*, having returned his *scroll* to his chest pocket, offered fervent thanks to *God* for His directing of his eyes to the place where it had fallen. So with joy and tears he now focused upon moving ahead in his journey.

But oh how nimbly did he now go up the rest of the *Hill*! Yet before he reached the top, the sun began to set upon *Christian*; so again he was made to painfully recall the foolishness of his delaying sleep, for he ought to have been much farther ahead by now. For this reason he continued to condole [*grieve*] with himself: "Ah, how sinful you are, oh sleep! On account of you my journey in the light has been overcome by the night! Now I must walk without the sun while darkness covers my path; now I must hear the voice of doleful creatures because of my negligent sleep!"

Now he also remembered the account of *Timorous* and *Mistrust*, how they had told him of their fear at the sight of the lions.[5] Then *Christian* mused with himself, "These beasts prowl in the night seeking their prey, so if they should meet with me in the dark, how can I possibly avoid being torn in pieces?" Hence he nervously went on his way; but while he was mourning over this fearful turn of events, on lifting up his eyes he noticed a very regal palace directly ahead of him. Now the name of it was the *Palace Beautiful*, and it stood just to one side of the highway.[6]

---

5 *Prov. 22:13; 26:13.*

6 *Ps. 48:2, 13.*

14

CHRISTIAN MEETS LION-SIZED OPPOSITION

SO I saw in my dream that *Christian* hurried along toward the *Palace* since he hoped to obtain lodging there. Now before he had gone very far, he entered into an extremely narrow passage which was only a furlong away from the porter's lodge. And carefully proceeding along this restricted part of the highway, he perceived, not far ahead, two lions that seemed to stand in his way. Then *Christian* realized, "Now I see the danger that caused *Mistrust* and *Timorous* to turn back and flee," (though he did not detect the chains that restricted these ferocious beasts). As a result he was filled with fear and contemplated going back with them, for at that moment he thought that nothing but death was ahead of him.

But the porter named *Watchful*[1] at the *Palace* lodge, in noticing that *Christian* hesitated, as if contemplating a retreat on account of the prospect of death ahead of him, called out to him saying, "Are your strength and courage so small? Don't be so afraid of the lions since they are in fact chained; their being there is for the purpose of testing your faith at this point in your journey, as well as for the discovery of those who are faithless.[2] So keep in the middle of the path and you will not be harmed."

Then I saw that *Christian* went forward on his way, though trembling because of his fear of the lions; yet he was careful to follow the directions of the porter. Yes, the lions roared and snarled, but they were unable to harm him. As a result, he joyously clapped his hands and went on till he stood before the *Palace* gate where the porter awaited him.

---

1 Mark 13:34-35; *Heb. 13:17.*

2 *I Pet. 1:7.*

15

CHRISTIAN RESIDES AT THE PALACE BEAUTIFUL

THEN *Christian* spoke to the porter, "Sir, what is the purpose of this house? And may I reside here for the night?" The porter answered, "This house was built by the *Lord* of the *Hill*, and he built it for the relief and security of pilgrims."[1] The porter also asked from where he had come and where he was going.

CHRISTIAN: I have come from the *City of Destruction* and am going to *Mount Zion*; but because the sun has now set, I would like to stay here for the night, if you are willing.

PORTER: What is your name?

CHRISTIAN: My name is now *Christian*, though it was *Graceless* to begin with. I was born of the race of *Japheth* who *God* will persuade to dwell in the tents of *Shem*.[2]

PORTER: But how has it happened that you have arrived so late since the sun has already set?

CHRISTIAN: I ought to have been here sooner, but oh wretched man that I am![3] I overslept at the *Shady Resting-place* that is located on the side of the *Hill Difficulty*. Yet in spite of that I would have been here much sooner, except that as I slept I lost my *scroll* of certification and reached the top of the *Hill* without it. Then searching for it, I was dismayed to find it had gone; so I was forced, with heaviness of heart, to return to the place where I overslept; then on recovering it, I pressed forward once again and thus have come this far.

PORTER: Well, I will call out for one of the virgins who live here; if your conversation is to her liking, she will invite you to join the rest of the family, that is in accordance with the rules of the house.[4]

---

1 *The Palace Beautiful represents a faithful Nonconformist church.*

2 Gen. 9:27; *Rom. 11:11-32.*

3 *Rom. 7:24.*

4 *Christian is to be considered for church membership.*

So the porter *Watchful* rang a bell, at the sound of which a dignified and beautiful lady named *Discretion* came to the door of the house and asked why she had been called.[5] The porter answered, "This man is on a journey from the *City of Destruction* to *Mount Zion*; but being weary and seeing the sun has now set, he asked me if he might stay the night here. So I told him I would call you, and that after some discussion with him, you would decide what seemed best according to the rules of the house."

Then she asked him from where he had come and where he was going; so he told her. She also asked him how he had entered into the way, and he told her. Then she asked him what he had seen and encountered along the way, and he told her. Finally, she asked his name, and to this he replied, "It is *Christian*, and I now have an even greater desire to reside here tonight because, according to what I now understand, this place was built by the *Lord* of the *Hill* for the relief of pilgrims."[6] So she smiled, though tears welled up in her eyes.

Then after a little hesitation she said, "I will call here two or three more of the family." So she ran to an inner door and called out to *Prudence* [*wisdom*], *Piety* [*spiritual devotion*], and *Charity* [*love*] who, after a little more conversation with him, invited *Christian* inside to meet the rest of the family. As a result, many of the residents met him in the lobby and warmly beckoned, "Come in, you who are blessed of the *Lord*;[7] this house was built by the *Lord* of the *Hill* for the express purpose of entertaining pilgrims such as yourself."[8] Then *Christian* bowed his head in acknowledgment and followed them into the main part of the house.

So when he had come inside and sat down, they gave him something to drink; then they all agreed that until supper was ready, it would be a profitable use of their time if one or two of them should have conversation with *Christian* about some

---

5 *Prov. 2:11.*

6 *Christian has a healthy desire for church fellowship.*

7 *Gen. 24:31.*

8 *I Cor. 3:9-17; I Tim. 3:15; I Pet. 2:5-10.*

specific matters. So *Piety*, *Prudence*, and *Charity* were appointed to have discussion with him; and so they began.

PIETY: Come now good *Christian*, since we have been so loving toward you by receiving you into our house tonight, let us profitably spend time amongst ourselves by talking with you about all the things that have happened to you on your pilgrimage.

CHRISTIAN: Why I would be more than willing to speak this way; how glad I am that you prefer this type of conversation.

PIETY: What moved you at first to take upon yourself the life of a pilgrim?

CHRISTIAN: I was driven out of my native country by a dreadful sound that was in my ears, that is the persistent conviction that unavoidable destruction would consume me, that is if I continued to live in the *City of Destruction*.

PIETY: But how did it happen that you came out of your country in this direction?

CHRISTIAN: It was as *God* would have it, for when I was fearful of destruction hovering over me, I did not know which way to go; but through providence there came a man, even to me as I was trembling and weeping, whose name was *Evangelist*. And he directed me toward the *Wicket-gate* otherwise I would not have found it. And so at the same time he pointed out the way that has led me directly to this *Palace*.

PIETY: But did you not come by way of the house of the *Interpreter*?

CHRISTIAN: Yes, and the things that I saw there were truly memorable; they will stay with me as long as I live, and especially three scenes. They were, how *Christ*, in opposition to *Satan*, maintains his work of grace in the heart; how the man in the iron cage had sinned himself quite out of the hope of *God's* mercy; and also the dream of the man who thought in his sleep that the day of judgment had come.

PIETY: Why, did you hear this man tell about his dream?

CHRISTIAN: Yes, and I thought it was such a dreadful revelation. It made my heart ache as he was telling about it. Nevertheless, I am glad that I heard it.

PIETY: Was that all that you saw at the house of the *Interpreter*?

CHRISTIAN: No, for he took me to where I saw a stately *Palace*, and how people dressed in gold were in it; and how a courageous man strode forth and cut his way through the armed men that stood in the doorway to keep him out; and how he was commanded to come inside and win eternal glory. My mind and heart were totally ravished [*enthralled*] at the sight of these things. I could have stayed at that good man's house for a year, except that I knew that I still had a distance to go.

PIETY: And what else did you see along the way?

CHRISTIAN: See! Why I had only gone a short distance ahead when I saw, as it were in my mind, a man hang bleeding on a tree; and the very sight of him made my burden fall from off my back, which load had caused me to groan so much; yes, it did actually drop from off my back! It was so astonishing for me because I had never seen such a thing before. Yes, and while I was looking up at that tree, for I could not stop looking, three *Shining Ones* came to me: one of them declared that my sins had been forgiven: another stripped me of my rags and gave me this embroidered coat,[9] as you can see; and the third set a visible mark upon my forehead, and gave me this sealed *scroll* which I keep in my chest pocket.

PIETY: But you saw even more than this, did you not?

CHRISTIAN: The things that I have told you about were the best: yet I saw some other interesting matters, namely three men lying asleep beside the way with shackles upon their heels; their names were *Simple*, *Sloth*, and *Presumption*, and it was near impossible to awaken them. I also met with *Formalist* and *Hypocrisy* who came tumbling over the wall to go, as they pretended, to *Mount Zion*. But they were soon lost, even as I warned them that they would be; they simply would not believe. However, it was most difficult of all getting up this *Hill*, and equally as distressing in passing by the mouths of those lions. Truly, if it had not been for that good man, your porter *Watchful* who stands at the gate, it is probable that I would have eventually turned around and fled down the *Hill*. But now I do thank *God* that I am here, and I thank you for welcoming me.

---

9 *Exod. 28:4; Ezek. 16:10.*

Then *Prudence* thought of asking *Christian* a few questions; so she asked him to answer.

PRUDENCE: Do you sometimes think of the country from which you originally came?

CHRISTIAN: Yes, but with much shame and loathing. Truly, if I had a deep yearning for that country, then I might well have taken the opportunity to return. But now my heart desires a better country, that is a heavenly realm.[10] Therefore I prefer to press on.

PRUDENCE: Do you not still carry with you in your mind some recollection of the things that you were formerly involved with?

CHRISTIAN: Yes, but greatly against my will, and especially those inward and carnal reasonings which all of my countrymen, as well as myself, were delighted to revel in. But now all those things only grieve me; and should I be able to choose only what I think, I would choose never to think of those carnal things anymore. But when I would be doing that which is best, still that which is worse remains with me.[11]

PRUDENCE: Do you not sometimes find that personal carnality is vanquished when at other times it was of great trouble to you?

CHRISTIAN: Yes, but those times of conquest over carnality are infrequent, though when they do occur such hours are truly golden.

PRUDENCE: When you experience these precious times in which carnal annoyances are vanquished, can you remember by what means these triumphs were obtained?

CHRISTIAN: Yes, when I meditate upon what I saw at the *Cross*, that will do it; and when I look at my embroidered coat, that will do it; also when I look inside the *scroll* that I carry in my chest pocket, that will do it; and when my thoughts are warmly stimulated about where I am going, that will do it.

PRUDENCE: And what is it that makes you so desirous of going to *Mount Zion*?

---

10 Heb. 11:15-16.

11 *Rom. 7:14-25.*

CHRISTIAN: Why there I hope to see living he who hung dead on the *Cross*; and there I hope to be rid of all those things within me that remain a constant annoyance. At the *Celestial City* they say there is no death,[12] and there I shall dwell with the type of companions that I like best. For to tell you the truth, I love my *Lord* because he released me of my burden, and I am weary of my inward sickness. In view of these circumstances, I would much prefer to be where I shall die no more and my companions shall continually cry, "Holy, Holy, Holy."[13]

Then said *Charity* to *Christian*, "Do you have a family? Are you a married man?"

CHRISTIAN: I have a wife and four small children.[14]

CHARITY: And why did you not bring them along with you?

CHRISTIAN: (Then weeping) Oh how willingly I would have done so, but all of them were utterly opposed to my going on pilgrimage.

CHARITY: But you should have talked to them, and attempted to show them the danger of remaining behind.

CHRISTIAN: And this I did, and explained what *God* had revealed to me concerning the destruction of our *City*. But I seemed to them as one that told a joke, and as a consequence they did not believe.[15]

CHARITY: And did you pray to *God* that he would give them understanding of your warning?

CHRISTIAN: Yes, and that with considerable warmth of affection, for you must understand that my wife and poor children were very precious to me.

CHARITY: But did you tell them of your own sorrow and fear of destruction? For I expect that the prospect of destruction was very evident to you.

CHRISTIAN: Yes, over and over and over again. Most likely they could recognize the fear portrayed in my face, and particularly in my tears and trembling, on account of my alarm

---

12 Isa. 25:8; Rev. 21:4.

13 *Isa. 6:3; Rev. 4:8.*

14 *This was true of Bunyan as he wrote The Pilgrim's Progress.*

15 Gen. 19:14.

at the reality of impending judgment. Yet all of this was not sufficient to persuade them to come with me.

CHARITY: But what reasons did they offer? Why would they not come with you?

CHRISTIAN: For one thing, my wife was afraid of losing this world; furthermore my children were absorbed with the foolish delights of youth. So because of these and many other distractions, they left me to wander alone in this distressed frame of mind.

CHARITY: But for all of your talk and persuasive efforts to have your loved ones depart with you, did your empty manner of life nevertheless dissuade them from acting upon your advice?

CHRISTIAN: To be sure, I cannot commend my life, for I am only too well aware of my countless failings: in this regard I also know that a man, by means of his manner of life, may soon negate whatever arguments or good reasons he may strenuously present to others for their good. Even so, I can honestly confess how very careful I was to avoid giving them any reason, that is with regard to disgraceful behavior on my part, for not going on pilgrimage. In fact, for this cautious attitude they would criticize me and tell me I was too precise [*puritanical*] in denying myself things, for their sakes, in which they saw no wrong. And I think I can rightly say that if there was anything that really did hinder them, it was my own great tenderness in being careful not to sin against *God*, or do any wrong to my neighbor.

CHARITY: Even as you say, *Cain* hated his brother because his own works were evil and those of his brother were righteous.[16] And if your wife and children were offended at you for this reason, then they show themselves to be unyielding toward that which is good; and so you have delivered your soul from accountability for their blood.[17]

Then I [*Bunyan*] saw in my dream that they all sat talking together until supper was ready. So when the meal was prepared, they sat down to eat.[18] Now the table was set with fat

---

16 *Gen. 4:1-15*; I John 3:12.

17 Ezek. 3:19.

18 *A representation of the Lord's Supper or Communion. I Cor. 11:23-29.*

[*good, substantial*] things, and with wine that was well refined;[19] and all of their conversation at the table was about the *Lord* of the *Hill*. For instance, they talked about what he had done and the purpose of it, and why he had built that *House*: and from what they said I understood that he had been a great warrior, and that he had fought with and slain he who had the power of death, though not without great danger to himself.[20] And for this reason I was led to love him only all the more.

For as they said, and as I believe (said *Christian*), he did it with the loss of much blood. But that which put the glory of grace into all which he did was the fact that he did it out of pure love for his country. And besides this, there were some of the household that said they had seen and spoken with him following his death on the *Cross*; and they further testified, having received it from his own lips, that he was such a lover of pilgrims that his likeness was not to be found from the east to the west.

Moreover, they gave an instance of what they had just declared, and it was that he had stripped himself of his glory so that he might do this for the poor;[21] and that they had heard him affirm that he would not dwell in *Mount Zion* alone. Furthermore, they said that he had made many pilgrims into princes, even though they were born beggars and their nature originated from the dunghill.[22]

So they discoursed together until late at night; and after they had committed themselves in prayer to their *Lord* for protection, they each went to bed. For the pilgrim they provided a large upstairs chamber [*bedroom*] with windows that opened toward the rising of the sun.[23] The name of the room was *Peace*,

---

[19] *Isa. 25:6.*

[20] Heb. 2:14-15.

[21] *II Cor. 8:9; Phil. 2:5-11.*

[22] I Sam. 2:8; Ps. 113:7.

[23] *Mark 14:15.*

and there he slept until the next day dawned.[24] Then on arising that morning, he joyfully sang,

> Where am I now? Is this the love and care
> Of *Jesus*, for the men that pilgrims are?
> Thus to provide! That I should be forgiven!
> And dwell already the next door to *Heaven*.

Now in the morning they all got up, and after some further discourse, they told *Christian* that he should not depart until they had showed him the rarities [*distinctive features*] of that place. And first they took him into the study where they pointed out records of the greatest antiquity; in these, as I recall in my dream, they first explained the pedigree of the *Lord* of the *Hill*, that he was the son of the *Ancient of Days*[25] and came [*was begotten*] by an eternal generation.[26] Also, here was more fully recorded the acts [*deeds*] that he had accomplished, and the names of many hundreds that he had recruited into his service; and how he had placed them in habitations [*mansions, residences*] that would never pass away, whether by means of earthly decay or the passing of time.[27]

Then they read to him some of the notable deeds that many of his servants had done, such as how they had subdued kingdoms, accomplished righteousness, obtained promises, stopped the mouths of lions, quenched the violence of fire, and escaped the edge of the sword. Yet in weakness they were made strong; thus they became more valiant in fight and turned to flight the armies of foreign enemies.[28]

Furthermore they read in another part of the *House Records* where it was revealed how willing their *Lord* was to receive into his favor any person of whatever kind, though they had previously offered deep insult to his holy character and great accomplishments. Here also were to be found a variety of

---

24 *II Cor. 13:11.*

25 *Dan. 7:9, 13, 22.*

26 *Ps. 2:7.*

27 *Ps. 21:3-4; John 14:2-3.*

28 Heb. 11:33-34.

historic documents concerning other famous events; and these *Christian* viewed as well. There were also things ancient and modern to be seen, along with prophecies and predictions concerning matters that are certain to be fulfilled, both to the dread and amazement of enemies as well as the comfort and relief of pilgrims.

The next day they led him into the *Armory* where they showed him a great variety of military weapons which their *Lord* had specially provided for pilgrims. There was the *Sword*, *Shield*, *Helmet*, *Breastplate*, *All-Prayer*, and *Shoes* that would never wear out.[29] Moreover, there was enough of this equipment in store to outfit as many men for the service of their *Lord* as there are multitudes of stars in the heavens.

They also showed him some of the military equipment with which many of his servants had done wonderful things. Here was *Moses'* rod,[30] the hammer and nail with which *Jael* slew *Sisera*,[31] the pitchers, trumpets, and lamps as well, with which *Gideon* put to flight the armies of *Midian*.[32] Then they showed him the oxgoad used by *Shamgar* to slay six hundred men.[33] They also showed him the jawbone with which *Sampson* did such mighty feats;[34] moreover they showed him the sling and stone with which *David* slew *Goliath* of *Gath*.[35] There was also on display the sword with which their *Lord* would eventually use to kill the *Man of Sin*, on that day of final victory over this predator.[36] Besides these they showed *Christian* many excellent things that so delighted him. So this day being concluded, they all went to bed once again.

---

29 *Deut. 29:5; Eph. 6:14-18.*

30 *Ex. 4:1-5, 17, 20; 7:8-12.*

31 *Judg. 4:17-22.*

32 *Judg. 7:16-23.*

33 *Judg. 3:31.*

34 *Judg. 15:14-17.*

35 *I Sam. 17:38-51.*

36 *II Thess. 2:3-8; Rev. 13:1-10.*

Then I saw in my dream that on the next day the pilgrim arose expecting to press forward on his journey. But the *Palace* company invited him to stay with them yet one more day. They added, "We will, if the day is clear, show you the *Delectable Mountains*. These will further add to your comfort because they are much nearer to the *Celestial City* than your present location." So *Christian* agreed to stay.

When the next morning had come, they took *Christian* to the top of the *Palace* and directed him to look south; in doing this he beheld, a great distance away, a very pleasant section of mountainous country.[37] There he saw beautiful woods, vineyards, fruit trees of all sorts; there were also flowers, as well as springs and fountains; in all it was very appealing to look upon. So he asked the name of this country and they said it was *Immanuel's Land*; they further explained that for true pilgrims, it was of the same character as the *Hill* on which their *Palace* was located. Then they announced, "When you arrive at that place, there resident shepherds will direct your eyes toward the near sight of the very gate of the *Celestial City*."

Now he decided to prepare himself for moving ahead once again. "But first," said his companions, "let us return to the *Armory*." So they did this, and when *Christian* entered the room, he was equipped from head to foot with fully tested weapons lest he should encounter assaults along the way.[38] Thus having been well accoutered [*outfitted*], he was escorted by his friends to the *Palace* gate where he asked the porter if he had seen any other pilgrims pass by. To this the porter answered, "Yes."

CHRISTIAN: Do tell me if you know him by name?

PORTER: I did ask his name and he told me it was *Faithful*.

CHRISTIAN: Oh, I know him; he was a fellow-countryman and a near neighbor. He comes from the *City of Destruction* where I was born. How far ahead do you think he may have gone?

PORTER: By this time he has probably passed beyond the bottom of the *Hill*.

---

37 Isa. *8:8*; 33:16-17.

38 *Eph. 6:11-17.*

CHRISTIAN: Well, my good porter, may the *Lord* be with you and increase his blessings on you because of the kindness you have shown to me.

Then the pilgrim began to move forward. But *Discretion*, *Piety*, *Charity*, and *Prudence* all agreed that they would accompany him down to the bottom of the *Hill*. So they went on together while reviewing their former discussions, that is until they came to the foot of the *Hill*. Then said *Christian* on his way down, "I can now appreciate that while it was difficult coming up this *Hill*, so far as I can see it is even more dangerous going down." To this *Prudence* responded, "Yes, you are right; for it is a hard matter for a man to go down into the *Valley of Humiliation* as you are now doing, and not slip in any way. Hence it is for this reason that we decided to escort you this far." So they continued to go down, though very warily; yet in spite of this *Christian* did slip once or twice.[39]

Then I saw in my dream that when the pilgrim had reached the bottom of the *Hill*, his good companions gave him a loaf of bread, a bottle of wine, and a cluster of raisins;[40] then they bid him farewell. So he went on his way.

Discretion

[39] *Ps. 94:18.*

[40] *I Sam. 30:11-12.*

16

CHRISTIAN ENTERS INTO BATTLE WITH APOLLYON

NOW *Christian* had not gone far in this *Valley of Humiliation* before he was severely tested, for he noticed a very foul fiend coming over the field to meet him; his name was *Apollyon* [*Destroyer*].[1] At this *Christian* became afraid and immediately pondered whether he ought to retreat or stand his ground. But on further consideration he realized that he had no armor on his back, and therefore to expose himself there in fleeing would probably give this foe the advantage with his use of piercing darts.[2] So he determined to risk confrontation with this enemy. For he further thought, "If I only had in mind the saving of my life, then it would still be best to stand my ground."

So he continued on, and *Apollyon* met him. Now this monster was exceedingly hideous to behold; he was clothed with scales like a fish of which he was most proud; he had wings like a dragon, feet like a bear, and out of his belly belched forth fire and smoke through a mouth like that of a lion.[3] When he drew near to *Christian*, he looked down upon him with a contemptuous, sneering expression, and then commenced to question him.

APOLLYON: From where have you come, and where are you going?

CHRISTIAN: I have come from that place of all evil, the *City of Destruction*, and am heading toward the *City of Zion*.

APOLLYON: So from this I conclude that you are one of my subjects since the whole of that region belongs to me; I am its prince and god![4] This being true, then how is it that you have

---

1 *Rev. 9:11.*

2 *Eph. 6:16.*

3 *Job 41:15-17, 20-21; Dan. 7:5; I Pet. 5:8; Rev. 9:17; 12:3-17; 13:2.*

4 *John 12:31; 14:30; 16:11; II Cor. 4:4.*

run away from your king? Were it not for the fact that my plan is for you to serve me further, I would, right now, strike you to the ground with one smashing blow.

CHRISTIAN: It is true that I was born in your territories, but your employment was hard; and your wages were such that a man could not properly live on them since the wages of sin is death.[5] Therefore when I came to adulthood, I did what other thoughtful people ought to do, and that is seek for better employment.

APOLLYON: You understand that no prince worthy of the name will easily release his subjects; and so neither will I let you go at this time. But since you have complained of your duties and salary, let me encourage you to return; I personally promise that every attempt will be made by our government to improve your wages.[6]

CHRISTIAN: But I have yielded my loyalty to another, even to the *King* of princes; so in all fairness, how can I possibly return to you?

APOLLYON: You have done that which the proverb describes, namely, "exchanged a bad for a worse."[7] Though it is quite common for those who profess themselves to be his servants, after a while, to slip away from his employment and again return to me. Do this and I assure you that all will be well.

CHRISTIAN: But I have given him my faith and sworn allegiance; so how then can I go back on my word and not be hanged as a traitor?

APOLLYON: You did the very same thing to me! Nevertheless, I am willing to let the past be forgotten if you will simply turn once more and go back to the *City of Destruction.*[8]

CHRISTIAN: What I promised you then was in my nonage [*as an immature youth*]; and besides this, I regard my *Prince*, under whose banner I now stand, as able to absolve me of your charges; and even further, he is able to pardon whatever I did in

---

5 Rom. 6:23.

6 Apollyon's flattery.

7 Apollyon undervalues Christ's service.

8 Apollyon pretends to be merciful.

serving you. And besides all this, oh you destroying *Apollyon*, to be perfectly truthful, I like his employment, his wages, his servants, his government, his company and country infinitely more than yours. Therefore, stop trying to change my mind and leave me alone; I am the *Lord's* servant and I am determined to follow him.

APOLLYON: That is all very well; but consider what it will be like when your spirit is low and at the same time you have much to encounter in the way you are going. You are aware that, for the most part, his servants come to a wretched end because they are transgressors against me and my ways. How many of them there are who have been shamefully put to death! And furthermore, while you count his employment better than mine, yet he has never come from his heavenly residence to rescue any of his servants out of our hands. On the other hand, all the world well knows that I have, so many times, used my power and fraudulent schemes to deliver those who have faithfully served me; even when they were captured by he and his followers, still I have rescued them, and so I will also deliver you.

CHRISTIAN: His present restraint in delivering them is for the purpose of testing their love, that is proving whether they will be loyal to him to the end. And as for the sorry end that you declare is their destiny, why they are assured of receiving future glory. In fact they do not expect present deliverance; rather they are content to wait for their glory in the future, and then they shall certainly have it when their *Prince* comes in glory along with the angels.[9]

APOLLYON: But you have already been unfaithful in serving your new *Lord*, so how is it possible for you to receive any wages from him?

CHRISTIAN: Tell me, oh *Apollyon,* in what ways have I been unfaithful to him?

APOLLYON: Very soon after leaving the *City of Destruction*, you were quickly discouraged when you almost drowned in the *Slough of Despond*. You made several wrong attempts to be rid

---

[9] *Matt. 25:31; II Thess. 1:7.*

of your burden, whereas you should have waited until your *Prince* relieved you of it himself. Through shameful oversleeping, you lost a very precious personal possession; also you were nearly persuaded to turn back at the sight of those fierce lions; and when you converse, as you travel, of what you have heard and seen, your inward desire is for personal glory with regard to everything that you say or do.[10]

CHRISTIAN: All that you say is true; in fact there is much more that you have left out. But the *Prince* who I serve and honor is very merciful and most willing to forgive;[11] but besides this, these misdemeanors were committed in your territory where I was educated in them; and as a consequence I have grieved over them and repented of ever doing such things. Furthermore, I have received a full pardon regarding these crimes from my *Prince*.

APOLLYON: (In a furious rage) I am an enemy of this *Prince* of yours: I hate his person, his laws, and his people: for this reason I have purposely come out here to oppose you.

CHRISTIAN: *Apollyon*, be very careful what you are doing, for I am in the *King's* highway, that is the way of holiness;[12] so watch yourself.

APOLLYON: (Now defiantly astride the whole width of the way) I am void of fear in this matter, so prepare yourself to die, for I swear by my infernal den [*of iniquity*] that you shall go no further; here I will spill your soul!

At this *Apollyon* was quick to throw a flaming dart directly at his breast; but *Christian* used the shield that was in his hand and deflected it, and so avoided this danger. Then in response, *Christian* drew his sword since he now realized it was time to stir himself. But *Apollyon* swiftly hurled a hail of darts that, notwithstanding all the skill that *Christian* could muster to avoid, yet inflicted wounds on his head as well as his hand and

---

[10] *Zech. 3:1-5; Rev. 12:10.*

[11] *Ps. 86:5.*

[12] *Num. 20:17-19; 21:22; Deut. 2:27; Isa. 35:8; 40:3.*

foot.[13] Now this assault caused *Christian* to retreat a little, so that *Apollyon* pressed more forcefully; yet *Christian* again took courage and resisted as courageously as he could. This agonizing combat extended beyond half a day, even until *Christian* was almost exhausted. For you should know that *Christian*, on account of his wounds, inevitably grew weaker and weaker.

Then *Apollyon*, recognizing his opportunity, began to press closer upon *Christian* and, now wrestling with him, heavily threw him to the ground. As a result, *Christian's* sword flew out of his hand. Then *Apollyon* gleefully exclaimed, "I am sure of you now," and immediately he drew close intending to inflict a mortal wound.

At this point *Christian* began to despair of staying alive.[14] But, as *God* would have it, while *Apollyon* was preparing his final blow so as to destroy this good man, yet *Christian* was enabled to nimbly stretch out his hand and regain a grip on his sword. At the same time he cried out, "Do not rejoice against me, oh my implacable enemy, for when I fall, I shall yet arise."[15] Then he gave *Apollyon* a deadly thrust which caused him to draw back as if he had received a fatal wound. Now in perceiving this, *Christian* moved in upon him while declaring, "Even so, we are more than conquerors through him who loved us."[16] As a result, *Apollyon* quickly spread out his dragon's wings and fled away so that *Christian* saw him no more.[17]

Now unless any man had seen and heard the intensity of this combat as I did, he could not possibly imagine the yelling and hideous roaring of *Apollyon*, as well as his dragon-like manner of speaking. On the other hand, what sighs and groans there were that burst forth from *Christian's* heart. During the whole encounter I never saw him give so much as one pleasant look,

---

13 Christian is wounded in his understanding [*head*], faith [*hand*], and conversation [*foot*]. *Lev. 8:23-24.*

14 *II Cor. 1:8.*

15 Mic. 7:8.

16 Rom. 8:37.

17 Jas. 4:7.

that is until he was aware of his wounding of *Apollyon* with his two-edged sword;[18] but then he smiled broadly and at the same time looked upward. However, on the whole, this was the most dreadful sight that I had ever seen.

So when the battle was over, *Christian* declared, "I will here give thanks to him who has delivered me out of the mouth of the lion, that is against *Apollyon*;"[19] and so he spoke with gratitude as follows:

> Great *Beelzebub*, the captain of this fiend,
> Designed my ruin; therefore to this end
> He sent him harnessed out, and he with rage
> That hellish was, did fiercely me engage.
> But blessed *Michael* helped me,[20] and I
> By dint [*blow*] of sword did quickly make him fly.
> Therefore to him let me give lasting praise,
> And thank and bless his holy name always.

Then there came to *Christian* a hand in which were some of the leaves of the *Tree of Life*, and taking these he applied them to the wounds that he had received in the battle; as a result he was immediately healed.[21] He also sat down at that same place to eat bread and drink from the bottle that had earlier been given to him. So being refreshed, he prepared himself for moving forward in his journey. Now his sword was already drawn in his hand, for he said, "I do not know if some other enemy may be near at hand."[22] Even so, he did not meet with any further opposition from *Apollyon,* that is throughout the remainder of this valley.

---

18 *Heb. 4:12.*

19 *II Tim. 4:17.*

20 *Dan. 10:13, 21; Rev. 12:7-9.*

21 *Rev. 22:2.*

22 *Eph. 5:15.*

17

CHRISTIAN CONFRONTS THE VALLEY OF THE SHADOW OF DEATH

NOW at the end of this valley there was another called the *Valley of the Shadow of Death*; and it was necessary for *Christian* to pass through it because the way to the *Celestial City* was in that direction. Now this valley was a very solitary and lonely place. The prophet *Jeremiah* describes it as, "A wilderness, a land of deserts and of pits, a land of drought and of the shadow of death, a land that no man" (except a *Christian*) "passes through, and where no man dwells."[1]

Now it was here that *Christian* was more severely tried than when he earlier engaged *Apollyon* in battle; and this will become evident in the following account.

So I [*Bunyan*] saw in my dream that, when *Christian* arrived at the borders of the *Valley of the Shadow of Death*,[2] two men met him there, namely children of those [*spies*] who had earlier delivered an evil report of the good [*Promised*] *Land,* and quickly determined to turn back.[3] To these *Christian* spoke as follows:

CHRISTIAN: Where are you going?

MEN: Oh back, yes definitely back to where we have come from! And frankly, we would have you do exactly the same, that is if you value either life or peace.

CHRISTIAN: Why? What is the matter with the way ahead?

MEN: You say "What is the matter"? Why we were pressing ahead just as you are presently doing, and reached as far as we dared. In fact had we gone only a little further on, it would have been impossible for us to return and bring this news to you.

CHRISTIAN: But what was it that you encountered?

---

1 Jer. 2:6.

2 *Ps. 23:4.*

3 Num. 13:1-33.

MEN: Why we were almost in the *Valley of the Shadow of Death*, but through good fortune we happened to look ahead and see the danger before we came too near.[4]

CHRISTIAN: But what was it exactly that you saw?

MEN: What did we see? Why it was the *Valley* itself being as dark as pitch.[5] We also saw there the hobgoblins, satyrs [*human/animal creatures*], and dragons of the pit;[6] in that *Valley* we also heard a continual howling and yelling, as if from people experiencing unspeakable misery, people who sat bound in affliction and irons. And over that *Valley* there hung the discouraging clouds of confusion while death spread its wings and hovered over it.[7] To sum up, it was a thoroughly dreadful sight; everywhere there was nothing but disorder.

CHRISTIAN: It is true that I have not yet seen what you describe. Nevertheless, the way ahead remains the chosen route by which I hope to arrive at my safe haven.[8]

MEN: If that is still to be your way, then so be it; but we will not any longer choose it as ours.

So *Christian* parted with the two men and continued to move forward, though his sword remained drawn, at the ready, for fear that he might be assaulted.[9]

Then I saw in my dream that, for the whole length of this *Valley*, on the right-hand side there was a very deep *Ditch*. And this was the same *Ditch* into which the blind have led the blind for endless ages, with the result that they all have miserably perished. Similarly on the left-hand side there was a very dangerous *Quagmire* into which, if even a good man fell, he could find no solid bottom for his feet to stand on. It was into this same *Quagmire* that *King David* once fell, and doubtless he

---

4 Ps. 44:19; 107:10.

5 *Bunyan describes his experience of such darkness in Grace Abounding, § 261.*

6 *Isa. 13:21; 34:14.*

7 Job 3:5; 10:22.

8 *Ps. 107:30*; Jer. 2:6.

9 *Eph. 5:15.*

would have been smothered there had it not been for the deliverance of He who was able to pull him out.[10]

Now at this place the way was extremely narrow, and for this reason *Christian* was severely tested as he pressed on. When in the dark he was careful to shun the *Ditch* on the right-hand side, but then he found himself in danger of stumbling into the *Quagmire* on the left-hand side. Moreover, when he attempted to escape the *Quagmire*, unless he was very cautious, he would find himself on the brink of falling into the *Ditch*. Yet *Christian* went on and it was here that I heard him sigh ever so bitterly; the reason was that besides the dangers mentioned above, the pathway here was so dark that often, when he lifted his foot to take a step forward, yet he did not know what he would find when he put it down.[11]

Now about in the middle of this *Valley*, here I noticed the location of the very mouth of *Hell*, it in fact being hard up against the narrow way. At the sight of this *Christian* wondered what he should do since so much flame and smoke were belching forth, accompanied with sparks and hideous noises. These fearful eruptions seemed quite unruffled concerning *Christian's* sword, as had been the case with *Apollyon*; so the trembling pilgrim found it necessary to resort to another weapon called *All-Prayer*.[12] In using this I was able to hear him cry out, "Oh *Lord*, I implore you to deliver my soul!"[13]

So *Christian* continued to pray in this manner for a long while; at the same time, as he crept along the way, the flames of *Hell* seemed to lick ever so close to him; he also heard doleful voices and rushes back and forth, so that sometimes he thought he would be torn in pieces or trodden under foot like mire in the streets.[14] While continuing to observe this frightful scene and hear such dreadful noises over the space of several miles, he

---

10 Ps. *51:1-19*; 69:14; *Matt. 15:14.*

11 *I Sam. 2:9.*

12 Eph. 6:18.

13 Ps. 116:4.

14 *II Sam. 22:43; Isa. 10:6; Mic. 7:10.*

came to a place where he thought he also heard a company of fiends who were approaching to meet him; this caused the pilgrim to muse over what it would be best for him to do.

Sometimes he had half a mind to go back; on the other hand he wondered if he might be at least half way through the *Valley*. He also recalled how he had already vanquished many a danger, and therefore he wondered if the perils of going back might be much greater than those encountered in going forward. So *Christian* decided to move ahead. Yet the fiends seemed to draw nearer and nearer; but when they seemed to be almost upon him, he cried out with such an impassioned cry, "I will walk in the strength of the *Lord*,"[15] that they drew back and ceased their approach.

One thing I should not avoid mentioning, by way of observation, is how poor *Christian* now appeared to be so confused; as I watched him, he did not even seem to know his own voice. Just when he came close to the mouth of the burning pit, one of the wicked ones sneaked up behind him, ever so softly, and whispered in his ear many suggestive and distressing blasphemies;[16] these he was convinced had originated from his own mind. Thus, in this manner, *Christian* was more sorely pressed in his journey than at any other time, since it troubled him to think that he could possibly blaspheme he who he loved so much. If he could have helped it, he need not have been so troubled; nevertheless, he did not have the discretion both to stop his ears and understand the real source of these blasphemies.

When *Christian* had traveled in this depressed condition for some considerable time, he then thought he heard the voice of a man on pilgrimage ahead of him, saying, "Though I walk through the *Valley of the Shadow of Death*, I will fear no evil, for You are with me."[17] As a result he felt very glad, and that for the following reasons:

---

[15] *Ps. 71:16.*

[16] *I Tim. 4:1.*

[17] Ps. 23:4.

First, because he gathered from what he heard that some who feared *God* were in this *Valley* as well as himself.

Second, since he understood that *God* was with them, even in such a dark and dismal place, then he reasoned that this invisible presence ought also to be with him, in spite of the hindrances of such a region.[18]

Third, for the hope that he entertained of eventually having fellowship, should he be able to overtake those ahead of him. So he went on and called out to the man who was ahead, though he did not know what to say in reply since he also had thought himself to be alone. Eventually the light of the morning dawned; at this *Christian* exclaimed, "He has turned the shadow of death into the morning."[19]

Now that a new day had come, he looked back, not out of a desire to return, but rather to see more clearly, by daylight, exactly what hazards he had traversed in the dark. So he saw more distinctly the *Ditch* that was on one side and the *Quagmire* that was on the other; he also perceived just how narrow the way was that lay between these perils; furthermore, he also identified the hobgoblins, satyrs, and dragons of the pit, even though they were now some distance from him. Apparently after daybreak they were reluctant to draw near, though he saw them in fulfillment of it being written, "He reveals deep things out of darkness, and brings to light the shadow of death."[20]

So *Christian* was greatly moved with his deliverance from all the dangers of his solitary journey thus far. Now these trials, though he feared them more than ever, yet had become more apparent to him because the light of day had exposed them. So with the sun now rising, this advantage offered *Christian* even more mercy; for it is to be noted that though the first part of the *Valley of the Shadow of Death* was dangerous, yet the second part ahead of him was, if at all possible, far more dangerous. This was because throughout the remainder of the *Valley* there were set innumerable snares, traps, gins [*catching devices*], and

---

18 Job 9:10.

19 Christian is glad at the break of day. Amos 5:8.

20 Job 12:22.

nets,[21] as well as there being countless pits, pitfalls, deep holes, and unsafe ledges in those depths.

Had it now been as dark as was formerly the case, though he possessed a thousand souls, yet they all would have been lost in this region. But, as I said, the sun was now rising. For this reason the pilgrim declared, "His candle shines on my head, and by his light I go through the darkness."[22]

Therefore in this light *Christian* came to the end of the *Valley*. Now I saw in my dream that at the end of this *Valley* there lay blood, bones, ashes, and the mangled bodies of men, even of pilgrims who had earlier come this way.[23] And while I was musing over what could be the reason for these remains, I noticed a short way ahead a cave in which lived two giants, *Pope* and *Pagan*; here they had lived for a long time, and by power and tyranny had cruelly put to death the men whose bones, blood, and ashes lay before him.

Yet at this place *Christian* passed by without much danger, and this somewhat surprised me. But subsequently I have learned that *Pagan* has been dead for many a day; and as for the other, though he is still alive, yet, on account of his old age and the many shrewd conflicts that he met with in his younger days, he has grown crazy and stiff in his joints. As a result he can now do little more than sit in the mouth of his cave, grinning at pilgrims as they go by and biting his nails, being frustrated because he cannot intercept them.

So I saw that *Christian* went on his way, though at the sight of the old man that sat at the mouth of the cave, he could not decide what to think, especially because *Pope* was unable to approach him, though he threateningly spoke, "You will never mend, until more of you are burned." But he held his peace and smiled as he passed by, though without suffering any harm. Then *Christian* sang:

---

21 *Gaming equipment.*

22 Job 29:3.

23 *As described in Foxe's Book of Martyrs.*

Oh world of wonders! (I can say no less)
That I should be preserved in that distress
That I have met with here! Oh blessed be
That hand that from it has delivered me!
Dangers in darkness, devils, *Hell*, and sin,
Did compass me, while I this vale was in:
Yes, snares, and pits, and traps, and nets did lie
My path about, that worthless silly I
Might have been caught, entangled, and cast down:
But since I live, let *Jesus* wear the crown.

Faithful

18
CHRISTIAN OVERTAKES AND CONVERSES WITH FAITHFUL

NOW as *Christian* went on his way, he came to a slight ascent which was specially designed so that pilgrims could more easily see ahead of them; therefore *Christian* went up and, looking forward, he saw *Faithful* in the distance intent on his journey. Then did *Christian* call out loudly, "Ho, ho, So-ho [*Here, here, look here*]; wait, let me catch up and I will be your companion." At this *Faithful* looked behind him, causing *Christian* to again cry out, "Wait, wait till I catch up with you." But *Faithful* replied, "No, I travel with my life at stake, and the *Avenger of Blood* is close behind."[1] This reply somewhat moved *Christian*, so mustering all his strength he quickly caught up with *Faithful* and in fact raced past him so that the last had become first! As a result *Christian* smiled with a sense of self-congratulation; he felt proud of now being ahead of his brother. Yet not paying attention to his feet, he suddenly stumbled and fell to the ground, and was unable to get up, that is until *Faithful* came up to help him.[2]

Then I saw in my dream that both of them went on very lovingly together; and they had delightful conversation about all of the things that had happened to them on their pilgrimage. So *Christian* spoke:

CHRISTIAN: My honored and well-beloved brother *Faithful*, I am glad that I have caught up with you, and that *God* has so tempered our spirits that we can walk as companions along such a pleasant pathway.

FAITHFUL: Dear friend, I had thought of enjoying your company even from our *Town*, but you did get quite a start on me; therefore I was forced to come this far on my own.

---

[1] *Num. 35:19, 21, 24-27; Deut. 19:6.*

[2] *Prov. 16:18; Eccles. 4:9-10; I Cor. 10:12; Gal. 6:1.*

CHRISTIAN: For how long did you stay in the *City of Destruction*, that is before you set out after me on your pilgrimage?

FAITHFUL: Till I could stay no longer; since after you had departed, there was so much discussion concerning the near prospect of our *City* being burned to the ground by means of fire from *Heaven*.

CHRISTIAN: Is that so? Did your neighbors really talk this way?

FAITHFUL: Yes, this sober conversation was in everybody's mouth, at least for a while.

CHRISTIAN: But tell me, were there no more than yourself who came away to escape the danger?

FAITHFUL: As I said, there was certainly a lot of talk going on, though I do not think that they really believed it. For in the heat of this exchange I heard some of them speak of you with ridicule. Your pilgrimage was contemptuously called a desperate journey, though I did believe, and still do, that the end of our *City* will be with fire and brimstone from above; so as a result I made my escape.

CHRISTIAN: Did you hear of any talk concerning neighbor *Pliable*?

FAITHFUL: Yes, *Christian*, for I heard that he accompanied you till he came to the *Slough of Despond;* there, as some have reported, he fell in. Even so he would not let on about this; but I am quite sure that he was thoroughly bedaubed [*foully covered*] with the dirt of that place.

CHRISTIAN: And what did the neighbors say to him?

FAITHFUL: Since his return he has been the subject of considerable derision, and that by all sorts of people. Some quite mock and despise him, while scarcely anyone will give him employment. He is now seven times worse than if he had never departed from the *City*.[3]

CHRISTIAN: But why is it that they were so set against him, especially since they also despised the way that he eventually abandoned?

---

[3] *Matt. 12:43-45.*

FAITHFUL: Oh they said "Hang him, since he is a turn-coat; he was not true to his profession." I think *God* has stirred up even his enemies to hiss [*jeer*] at him so as to make him a proverb [*standing example*], because he deserted the way.

CHRISTIAN: Did you ever talk with him before your departure?

FAITHFUL: I did meet him once in the streets, but he only leered at me from a distance on the other side, as if ashamed of what he had done; so I did not actually speak to him.

CHRISTIAN: Well, when I first set out on pilgrimage, I did have some hope for that man. But now I fear he will perish in the imminent destruction of the *City*, just as his case is described according to the true proverb, "The dog has turned to his vomit again, and the sow that was washed has gone back to her wallowing in the mire."[4]

FAITHFUL: They are my fears for him as well. But who can hinder that which is to be?

CHRISTIAN: Well neighbor *Faithful*, let us cease wondering about him, and rather talk of things that more immediately concern us. Tell me now, what have you met with and experienced having come thus far? Truly it would be a wonder worth recording if you had not met with at least some notable things.

FAITHFUL: I escaped the *Slough of Despond* which, I understand, you fell into; and so I reached the *Wicket-gate* without any danger, except that there I was propositioned by a woman named *Wanton* [*Promiscuous*] who intended to do me considerable harm.

CHRISTIAN: It was just as well you escaped her clutches. *Joseph* [*in Egypt*] was severely tested by her, though he escaped her just as you did; otherwise she would have cost him his life.[5] But what else did she do to you?

FAITHFUL: You cannot imagine, except through personal experience, just how flattering her tongue was; she pressed me hard to go with her by promising all sorts of sensual pleasure.

---

4 *Prov. 26:11*; II Pet. 2:22.

5 Gen. 39:11-13.

CHRISTIAN: But she did not promise you the enjoyment of a good conscience.

FAITHFUL: No, for you well understand that what she really offered was strictly carnal and fleshly.

CHRISTIAN: Thank *God* you have escaped her, since it is the abhorred of the *Lord* who shall fall into her ditch.[6]

FAITHFUL: True, but I am still not sure if I have totally escaped her pleading.

CHRISTIAN: Why I trust you did not agree to her solicitation, did you?

FAITHFUL: No, I did not defile myself with her, for I remembered an old writing which I had seen that declared, "Her steps descend down to *Hell*." So I shut my eyes to prevent myself from being bewitched with her seductive looks.[7] Then she suddenly became angry and abused me, at which I quickly departed from her.

CHRISTIAN: Did you meet with any other assaults as you went on your way?

FAITHFUL: When I came to the foot of the *Hill Difficulty*, I met a very old man who asked me, "Who I was and where I was going?" I replied that I was a pilgrim going to the *Celestial City*. Then he commented, "You look like an honest fellow. Will you consider the contentment that is available by living with me, and especially the wages I am prepared to offer?" Then I asked him his name and where he lived. He said that his name was *Adam the First*,[8] and that he resided in the *Town of Deceit*.[9] Then I enquired of him what his line of business was and what exactly the wages were that he offered. To this he responded that his employment offered many delights, and that his wages were full heirship in his family.

I further asked him details concerning the support of his household and the servants that he kept. So he explained that his household was maintained with a great variety of exotic

---

6 Prov. *7:1-27*; 22:14.

7 Job 31:1; *Prov. 6:25-27*; 5:5.

8 *Rom. 5:12, 17; I Cor. 15:45-47.*

9 Eph. 4:22.

dainties gleaned from the four corners of the world; further, his servants were his own children. Then I asked him how many children he had, and he replied that there were only three, all daughters, named *The Lust of the Flesh*, *The Lust of the Eyes*, and *The Pride of Life*,[10] and that I could marry them if I so wished. Then I asked how long I could expect to live with him, and he answered, as long as he himself lived.

CHRISTIAN: Well, and what agreement eventually came between the old man and yourself?

FAITHFUL: Why at first I felt somewhat inclined to go with the man because his manner was quite appealing. However, on looking at his forehead as I talked with him I saw inscribed there, "Put off the old man with his deeds."[11]

CHRISTIAN: How did you respond then?

FAITHFUL: Why it came burning hot into my mind that whatever he said, and however he flattered, yet when he lured me into his house, then he would sell me as a slave. So I insisted that he cease his talk since I had not the slightest intention of even going near the door of his house. Then he reviled me, and told me he would set a certain person onto me who would cause the way ahead to become bitter to my soul. So I turned to depart from him: but just as I was leaving to proceed on my journey, I felt him grasp hold of my flesh with such a deadly seizure that I felt he had torn away part of my body to himself. This made me cry out in pain, "Oh wretched man [*that I am*]!"[12] So I went on my way up the *Hill*.

Now when I had proceeded about halfway up, I looked behind me and saw someone coming after me, as swift as the wind; so he overtook me just about where the *Shady Resting-place* is located.[13]

CHRISTIAN: Yes, it was there that I sat down to rest myself; but being quite overcome with sleep, I lost my *scroll* there because it fell out of my chest pocket.

---

[10] I John 2:16.

[11] *Rom. 6:6; Eph. 4:22; Col. 3:9.*

[12] Rom. 7:24; *Gal. 5:17.*

[13] *Rom. 7:7-12.*

FAITHFUL: But my good brother, do hear me out. Just as soon as the man overtook me, without a word he struck me down and left me for dead. However, upon reviving a little from unconsciousness, I asked him why he had treated me so brutally. He indicated that is was on account of my secret inclination to heed old *Adam the First*; and with that he struck me another deadly blow on my chest and beat me down to the ground; so once again I lay at his feet as if dead. So when I regained consciousness, I pleaded with him for mercy; but he replied that he did not know how to show mercy, and then he knocked me down once more. Undoubtedly he would have completely finished me off had it not been for another person who came and demanded that he immediately cease with his assault.[14]

CHRISTIAN: Who was it that ordered him to stop?

FAITHFUL: At first I did not recognize him; but then as he passed by I noticed the holes in his hands as well as his side. Then I concluded that he was our *Lord*. So I continued on up the *Hill*.[15]

CHRISTIAN: That man who overtook you was *Moses*; he does not spare anyone, nor does he know how to show mercy to those who disobey his law.

FAITHFUL: I well know what you say to be true because this was not the first time that we had met. When securely living in the *City of Destruction*, it was he who came and threatened to burn down my house if I continued to live in that place.

CHRISTIAN: But did you not see the *House* that stood on the top of that *Hill*? It lay on the same side of the way where *Moses* met you.

FAITHFUL: Yes, and I saw the lions as well before I came to it, though it being noon, these beasts seemed asleep. So because I had so much of the day ahead of me, I passed by the *Porter* of that *House* and came down the other side of the *Hill*.

CHRISTIAN: When I spoke to him he told me that he had seen you pass by, though I wished that you had stayed awhile. Those at the *House* would have showed you so many

---

[14] *II Cor. 3:1-18.*

[15] *John 20:24-29.*

uncommon treasures that you would have hardly forgotten them in a lifetime. But do tell me, did you not meet with anyone in the *Valley of Humiliation*?

FAITHFUL: Yes, I met with a certain *Discontent*, who was so intent on persuading me to go back with him. He reasoned that the *Valley* ahead was dishonorable; further, to go ahead would be to displease all my friends such as *Pride*, *Arrogancy*, *Self-conceit*, *Worldly-glory*, and many others. These, he said, would be very much offended if I made such a fool of myself as to wade through this *Valley*.

CHRISTIAN: Well then; how did you answer him?

FAITHFUL: I told him that though all of these that he had named might claim to be my friends, and rightly so in terms of they're being relatives in the flesh, yet since becoming a pilgrim they had in fact disowned me; I also had rejected them, and therefore they were now no more to me than if they had never been family members.[16] Furthermore I told him that concerning this *Valley*, he had quite misrepresented it, "For before honor is humility, and a haughty spirit before a fall."[17] Therefore I explained that I would rather go through this *Valley* to obtain the honor which the wise so highly value than choose that which he esteemed to be worthy of our affections.

CHRISTIAN: Did you meet with anyone else in that *Valley*?

FAITHFUL: Yes, I met with *Shame*. But of all the men that I met with in my pilgrimage, I believe he bears the most inappropriate name. Although he would not accept it, a variety of evidence would more correctly suggest that he be called *Shameless*.

CHRISTIAN: Why do you say this? What did he say to you?

FAITHFUL: "What?" you ask. Why he objected against religion itself; he said that it was a pitiful, low, sneaking business for a man to esteem religion; he said that a tender conscience was an unmanly thing, and that for a man to watch over his words and ways so as to curtail that swaggering spirit which the heroes of this modern age freely parade, would be to make him

---

[16] *Gal. 6:14.*

[17] *Prov. 15:33; 16:18; 18:12.*

the most popular object of scorn. He also objected that very few of the mighty [*and influential*], the rich [*and famous*], and the [*intellectually*] wise were ever of my persuasion.[18] Further, on being invited to become fools, very few would freely venture the loss of all for the sake of a nebulous dividend.[19] Moreover, he objected to the base and low standard of living to which most pilgrims submitted themselves;[20] he sneered at their ignorance of the times in which they lived, and thus their lack of understanding of the physical sciences.

Yes, and he pressed me with a great deal more besides that which I have told you. He said that it was a shame to sit grieving and mourning under a sermon, and it was a shame to return home sighing and groaning. Further, he said that it was a shame to ask my neighbor for forgiveness on account of my petty faults, or to make restitution when I had stolen from somebody. He also said that religion caused a man to appear strange before the great of this world, for he became so concerned about a few petty vices spoken of in ever so serious terms, and this perception caused him to fraternize with the basest of society, solely on the ground of religious convictions. So he concluded, "And is not this a shame?"

CHRISTIAN: Then what did you say to him?

FAITHFUL: Say? Why at first I did not know what to say. Yes, he pressed me so hard that my face became red with embarrassment, as if I had myself become ashamed and nearly beaten down in defeat. But at last I began to consider that, "that which is highly esteemed among men is an abomination in the sight of *God*."[21] And I realized that this *Shame* was describing what men are about, but nothing concerning what *God* or the *Word of God* reveals. I thought as well that at the final day of judgment, we shall not be awarded death or life by the swaggering spirits of this modern world, but rather according to the wisdom and law of the *Highest*.

---

[18] I Cor. 1:26; 3:18.

[19] Phil. 3:7-8.

[20] John 7:48.

[21] Luke 16:15.

Therefore I thought, what *God* says is best, even though all the men in the world are against it. Seeing then that *God* prefers his religion, seeing that *God* prefers a tender conscience, seeing that those who yield themselves as fools for the kingdom of *Heaven* are wisest,[22] and that the poor man who loves *Christ* is richer than the greatest man in the world who hates him; then I said, "*Shame*, depart from me because you are an enemy of my salvation. Shall I listen to you contrary to my sovereign *Lord*? Otherwise, how shall I look him in the face at his coming? If I should now be ashamed of his ways and servants, how then can I expect the future blessing?"[23]

Nevertheless, this *Shame* was a bold villain indeed. I could hardly get rid of his clinging company; yes, he would even shadow me and continually whisper in my ear countless other weaknesses that he associated with religion. Eventually I told him that it would be in vain for him to continue in this manner, for those things which he derided were in fact those in which I boasted most of all. And so at last I was able to leave behind this persistent one.

Then when I had finally shaken him off, I began to sing:

> The trials that those men do meet withal
> That are obedient to the heavenly call,
> Are manifold and suited to the flesh,
> And come, and come, and come again afresh;
> That now, or sometime else, we by them may
> Be taken, overcome, and cast away.
> Oh let the pilgrims, let the pilgrims then,
> Be vigilant, and quit [*behave*] themselves like men.[24]

CHRISTIAN: My brother, I am glad that you did so bravely withstand this villain; for I think as you do, that of all the people you met, he undoubtedly has the wrong name. How bold he is to follow us in the streets and attempt to put us to shame before a watching world, that is to embarrass us concerning that which is good. For if he was not so audacious, he would never attempt

---

22 *I Cor. 1:18-25; 4:10.*

23 Mark 8:38.

24 *I Cor. 16:13.*

to be so bold. But let us resist him, for notwithstanding all of his bravado, he exclusively promotes himself as a fool. Remember that *Solomon* said, "the wise shall inherit glory, but shame shall be the promotion of fools."[25]

FAITHFUL: I think we ought to cry out to him for help against *Shame* so that we might be valiant for truth upon the *Earth*.[26]

CHRISTIAN: You certainly speak the truth. But did you meet with anybody else in that *Valley*?

FAITHFUL: No, I did not; for I experienced only sunshine along the remainder of that *Valley*, as well as through the following *Valley of the Shadow of Death*.

CHRISTIAN: Then it was far better for you since I fared much worse. Almost as soon as I entered the *Valley of Humiliation* I endured a prolonged and dreadful battle with that foul fiend *Apollyon*. Yes, I thought that he would surely kill me, and especially when he struck me to the ground and attempted to crush me; he seemed intent on breaking me in pieces. For as he threw me down, my sword flew out of my hand; then he exclaimed that he would now certainly destroy me. Yet I cried out to *God* and he heard me and delivered me from all of my troubles.[27]

Then I entered into the *Valley of the Shadow of Death*, and from then on had no light until almost halfway through that terrible place. Over and over again I felt sure that I would be killed there; but at last the morning broke, and with the rising of the sun I continued through that wilderness with far more ease and quiet.

---

[25] Prov. 3:35.

[26] *Jer 9:3. Refer to Valiant-for-Truth in Part Two of The Pilgrim's Progress.*

[27] *Ps. 34:6.*

19

CHRISTIAN AND FAITHFUL CONVERSE WITH TALKATIVE

MOREOVER, I saw in my dream that as they went on, *Faithful* happened to look to one side of the way and saw a man whose name is *Talkative*;[1] he was beside them though at a distance, for at this place it was wide enough for all of them to walk. He was a tall man and somewhat handsome if viewed from a distance. So *Faithful* introduced himself to this man in the following manner.

FAITHFUL: Why friend, which way are you going? Is it toward the heavenly country?

TALKATIVE: Yes, I am headed toward that very same place.

FAITHFUL: Then that is good. I do hope that we may have your fine company

TALKATIVE: Do be assured that I have every intention of being your companion.

FAITHFUL: Then join us right now and let us proceed together, and let us spend our time discussing some profitable things as we travel.

TALKATIVE: Certainly, for it is most enjoyable to talk with you, or others, of things that are good. I am so glad that I have met with those who are inclined toward such a good activity. For to tell you the truth, there are few to be found who care to spend their traveling time in this way; rather they eagerly choose to discuss things that are quite unprofitable, and this matter has often troubled me.[2]

FAITHFUL: Indeed that is a thing to be disturbed about; for what things are more worthy of the use of the tongue and mouth of men on *Earth* than those which concern the *God* of *Heaven*?

TALKATIVE: I do admire you for your attitude here, and especially your strong sense of conviction. Only let me add to

---

1 *Job 11:2; Prov. 10:19; Tit. 1:10, 16.*

2 *II Tim. 2:14.*

what you say; for what thing is so pleasant and so profitable in discussion as that which concerns the things of *God*. For instance, if a man really delights in such wonderful things, then what could be more pleasurable than talking about the history or mystery of certain matters? More specifically, if a man enjoys talking about miracles, wonders, or signs, then where shall he find such things so delightfully and sweetly recorded as in Holy Scripture?

FAITHFUL: That is very true, though to profit from the discussion of such things should be our real purpose.

TALKATIVE: That is exactly what I was getting at; for to talk of such things is most profitable since by so doing a man may get the knowledge of a variety of topics. For example, to speak generally, he may gain knowledge of the vanity of earthly things and the benefit of things above. But more particularly, he may learn of the necessity of the new birth, the insufficiency of our works, the need of *Christ's* righteousness, and so forth.

Besides, by this talk about religion, a man may learn what it is to repent, to believe, to pray, to suffer, or the like; further, by this type of conversation a man may learn what are the great promises and consolations of the gospel, and consequently gain much personal comfort. Moreover, by such discussion a man may learn how to refute false opinions, to vindicate the truth, and also to instruct the ignorant.

FAITHFUL: All of this is very true, and how glad I am to hear you say these things.

TALKATIVE: Alas, the lack of this perspective is the reason why so few understand the need of faith and the necessity of a work of grace in their soul so that they might obtain eternal life. So they ignorantly live according to the works of the law, by which means no man can enter the kingdom of *Heaven*.[3]

FAITHFUL: But do allow me to say that heavenly knowledge of these truths is the gift of *God*; no man can attain these things by means of human effort, let alone mere talk about them.

TALKATIVE: All of this I know very well. For a man can receive nothing except it has been given to him from *Heaven*; all

---

[3] *II Tim. 3:5, 7.*

is of grace, not of works. I could quote to you a hundred Scripture passages that confirm this.[4]

FAITHFUL: Well then, what is one good topic that we ought to talk about at this time?

TALKATIVE: Whatever you would like? I will talk of heavenly things or earthly things, of moral things or evangelical things, of sacred things or secular things, of past things or future things, of foreign things or domestic things, of essential things or incidental things, provided that any such discussion is profitable.[5]

FAITHFUL: (Now having become impressed with his newfound conversationalist, he stepped aside to *Christian*, who was walking by himself, and softly spoke to him) What a brave companion we have here! Surely this man will make a very excellent pilgrim.[6]

CHRISTIAN: (With a restrained smile) This man who you admire so much is able to beguile a multitude with his tongue, provided they are unfamiliar with him.

FAITHFUL: Then do you know him very well?

CHRISTIAN: Do I know him? Why yes, and even better than he knows himself.

FAITHFUL: Then seriously, do tell me who he is.

CHRISTIAN: His name is *Talkative* and he dwells in our former home *Town*; I am surprised that you do not know him, except for the reason that the *City of Destruction* is so large.

FAITHFUL: Who is his father? And exactly where does he live?

CHRISTIAN: He is the son of *Say-well* and he lives in *Prating* [*Foolish Chatter*] *-row*. All who really know him call him *Talkative of Prating-row*, and in spite of his eloquent manner of speaking, yet he remains a wretched fellow.[7]

FAITHFUL: Well he seems to me to be a rather attractive sort of person.

---

4 Oh brave Talkative! *John 3:27; Eph. 2:8-9.*

5 Oh brave Talkative! *Matt. 7:21; II Pet. 2:18.*

6 Faithful is beguiled by Talkative.

7 *Ps. 55:21.*

CHRISTIAN: Yes, he does appear that way to those who are not well acquainted with him; for he looks at his best from a distance, but close up he is quite ugly. Your description of him as a handsome man brings to mind what I have noticed with regard to the painter; his pictures look best from a distance; but up close they are noticeably unpleasant.[8]

FAITHFUL: But since you smile, can I conclude that you are offering merely an amusing comment?

CHRISTIAN: Even though I did smile, *God* forbid that I should make this a laughing matter, or that I should bring a false accusation against this man. I will simply reveal to you more about him. This man will accept any company, that is provided he is allowed to talk. Though this man will now talk with you, yet he will just as freely talk on the ale-bench [*enjoying tavern conversation*]. And the more drink he consumes, the more appropriate tavern talk he brings forth. Religion has no place in his heart, or home, or manner of living. All that he stands for is based upon his tongue; to make a noise with it is of the very essence of his religion.

FAITHFUL: What you say amazes me! Then I have been greatly deceived by this man.

CHRISTIAN: Deceived? Why you may be certain of it. Remember the proverb, "They say and do not: but the kingdom of *God* is not in word, put in power."[9] He talks of prayer, of repentance, of faith, and of the new birth; but he only knows how to talk about them. I have visited with his family and observed him both at home and far away, so I know what I say about him is the truth. His home is as empty of true religion as is the white of an egg void of flavor.[10] At his residence there is neither prayer nor any sign of repentance for sin. Yes, even an animal species serves *God* better than he. To all who know him, he is the very stain, reproach, and shame of true religion;[11]

---

8 *Matt. 23:25-28.*

9 Matt. 23:3; I Cor. 4:20; *I Thess. 1:5.*

10 *Job 6:6.*

11 Rom. 2:24-25.

because of his reputation, the neighborhood in the *City of Destruction* where he lives hardly has a good word to say about him. The common people there know him as, "A saint abroad and a devil at home."

His poor family can certainly agree with this because of their suffering of his extreme meanness and abusive language; even his servants are at a loss, in view of his unreasonableness, as to how they can satisfactorily fulfil their duties and address him. Men that do business with him say that, where a fair contract is sought, it is better to deal with a *Turk* [*barbarian trader*] than he. This *Talkative*, if it be possible, will defraud, beguile, and outsmart the most notorious of such foreign merchants.

In addition to this he brings up his sons to follow in his steps; and if he notices in any of them "a foolish timidness," as he caricatures the first appearance of a tender conscience, then he bawls them out as being stupid and blockheads; for this cause he will rarely employ them or recommend them to others. It is my opinion that he has, by his wicked lifestyle, caused many to stumble and fall; except that *God* should intervene, he will undoubtedly lead many more to ruin.[12]

FAITHFUL: Well, my brother, from what you say I am compelled to believe you, not only because you have personally known *Talkative*, but also because you give such a report with the right *Christian* attitude. I cannot imagine that you speak these things out of a malicious motive, but rather because of your love for the truth.

CHRISTIAN: Had I known him no more that you do, perhaps I might have thought of him as you did at first. Yes, and had I received such a report as this from the hands of those known to be the enemies of true religion, I would have thought it to be slanderous; sadly, the names and reputations of good men often suffer the lot of being defamed by bad men.

But in addition to all these things, yes I have knowledge to prove him guilty of a great many more sorry matters that are equally as bad. Besides, good men are ashamed of him; they can

---

[12] *Rom. 16:17-18.*

neither call him brother nor friend; to those who know him, the mere mention of his name in their midst makes them blush.[13]

FAITHFUL: Well, I see that saying and doing are two different things, and from now on I shall more carefully observe this distinction.[14]

CHRISTIAN: They are two things indeed, and are as diverse as are the soul and the body. For as the body without the soul is but a dead carcass, so saying that excludes doing is but a dead carcass as well.[15] The soul of true religion is the practical part. Pure and undefiled religion, in the sight of *God the Father*, is this, to visit the fatherless and widows in their affliction, and to keep oneself unspotted from the world.[16] *Talkative* is not aware of this; he thinks that hearing and saying alone will make a good Christian pilgrim, and thus he deceives his own soul.

Hearing is like the sowing of the seed; talking is not sufficient to prove that fruit is actually in the heart and life; and let us be perfectly clear that at the final day of doom, men shall be judged according to their fruit. It will not be said then, "Did you believe?" but, "Were you doers and talkers only?"[17] and accordingly they will be judged. The end of this world is compared to our earthly harvesting, and you know that men at harvest time regard nothing but fruit or grain. This is not to say that anything can be accepted without faith. But I speak to you this way to show you how insignificant the mere profession of *Talkative* will be at that day.

FAITHFUL: This brings to my mind that word from *Moses* in which he describes the clean type of beast. He is one that divides the hoof and chews the cud, not that divides the hoof alone or chews the cud alone. The rabbit chews the cud, yet is unclean because he does not divide the hoof. This truth is applicable to *Talkative* for he chews the cud, that is he seeks knowledge and chews upon the *Word*, but he does not divide the hoof, that is he

---

[13] *Rom. 2:24; II Pet. 2:1-2.*

[14] *Matt. 23:1-4.*

[15] *Jas. 2:26.*

[16] Jas. 1:22-27.

[17] Matt. 13:3-30, 36-43; 25:14-46.

does not separate himself from a sinful lifestyle; rather, as the rabbit, he retains the feet of a dog or bear, and therefore he is unclean.[18]

CHRISTIAN: As far as I know, you have spoken the true gospel sense of those texts, and I will add one further thing. *Paul* calls some men sounding brass and tinkling cymbal, and he includes great talkers as well; that is, as he expounds about these sayers elsewhere, he describes them as noisy and yet lifeless.[19] In being without life they lack true faith and the grace of the gospel. Consequently, these pilgrims shall never be placed in the kingdom of *Heaven* among those that are the children of life; and this remains true though their talk sounds like the voice of an angel.[20]

FAITHFUL: Well, I was not so fond of his company to start with, but now I am quite sick of it. What shall we do to be rid of him?

CHRISTIAN: Just take my advice and do as I tell you; then you will find that he will soon be sick of your company too, that is except *God* should touch his heart and convert it.

FAITHFUL: What would you have me to do?

CHRISTIAN: Why go to him and enter into some serious discussion about the power of true religion. And ask him plainly, after he has agreed with this topic, which he will readily do, whether this power of true religion has been set up in his heart, house, or daily behavior.

FAITHFUL: (Stepping forward again, he addresses *Talkative*) Come, my friend, what comfort do you have? How are you keeping?

TALKATIVE: Thank you; I am well. Though I thought we would have had considerable talk by now.

FAITHFUL: Well, if you agree, let us now have some useful discussion; and since you allowed me to nominate a question, let it be this: How does the saving grace of *God* show itself when it indwells the heart of a man?

---

18 Lev. 11:1-47; Deut. 14:1-21.

19 I Cor. 13:1-3; 14:7.

20 *Gal. 1:8.*

TALKATIVE: I notice then that our talk must be about the power of things? Well, this is a very good question, and I shall be more than willing to reply. So do accept my brief answer as follows. First, where the saving grace of *God* indwells the heart, there it causes a great outcry against sin. Secondly —

FAITHFUL: No, hold it there for a moment; let us consider each item one at a time. I think you should have rather said: It shows itself by inclining the soul to abhor its own sin.[21]

TALKATIVE: But why do you say this? What difference is there between crying out against, and the abhorring of [*personal*] sin?

FAITHFUL: Oh a great deal; a man may cry out against sin in principle; but he cannot abhor it except by virtue of his having a profound godly aversion to it. I have heard many cry out against sin in the pulpit, who yet can willingly embrace it in the heart, and house, and daily behavior.[22]

Joseph's mistress cried out with a loud voice, as if she were godly and virtuous; but notwithstanding this, she would have agreeably committed adultery with him.[23] Some cry out against sin, even as the mother cries out against her child in her lap, when she calls it a rude and naughty girl; then she quickly changes her mood and passionately devotes herself to hugging and kissing it.

TALKATIVE: I now see that you are trying to be clever and catch me out.

FAITHFUL: No, not I, for I am only attempting to set things straight. But what is the second thing that you would offer as proof of an evident work of grace in the heart?

TALKATIVE: It is a great knowledge of gospel mysteries.

FAITHFUL: This evidence should have been mentioned at the first, though it is false whether it be first or last. Knowledge, great knowledge may be obtained in the mysteries of the gospel, and yet no work of grace be present in the soul. Further, even if a man may have all knowledge, yet he may be nothing, and so

---

21 *Ps. 32:5; 51:4; Isa. 6:5; Lam. 1:18; Luke 5:8; I Tim. 1:15.*

22 *Matt. 23:25-28.*

23 Gen. 39:15.

consequently be no child of *God*.[24] When *Christ* said, "Do you know all these things?" and the disciples answered, "Yes." Then he added, "Blessed are you if you do them."[25] He does not offer this blessing in the mere knowing of his commands, but in the doing of them.[26]

Consequently there is a knowledge that is not accompanied with doing; it is found in the servant who knows his master's will, and yet fails to do it.[27] A man may know like an angel, and yet not be a Christian at all.[28] Therefore your proof is not valid. Indeed, to know is something which talkers and boasters find very pleasing. But to do is that which is pleasing to *God*.

Not that the heart can be good without knowledge. However, knowledge that is based upon the bare speculation of things and knowledge that is accompanied with the grace of faith and love, which constrains a man to do the will of *God* from the heart, these are not the same. The first of these is sufficient for the talker, but without the second the true Christian is not content. As the psalmist has written, "Give me understanding, and I shall keep thy law, yes, I shall observe it with my whole heart."[29]

TALKATIVE: You seem to be attempting to be clever again so as to catch me out; this has not become an edifying [*spiritually profitable*] conversation.

FAITHFUL: Well then, do offer another proof concerning how a work of grace in the heart is clearly evident.

TALKATIVE: No, not this time, for I now realize that we shall not agree.

FAITHFUL: Well, if you will not propose something, may I have your permission to speak in this way?

TALKATIVE: Do feel at liberty to go ahead.

---

24 I Cor. 13:2.

25 *John 13:12-17.*

26 *John 3:10; 14:21; Eph. 6:6; Jas. 1:25.*

27 *Matt. 21:28-31.*

28 *I Cor. 13:1-2.*

29 *Ps. 119:34.*

FAITHFUL: A true work of grace in the heart is recognized either by the person himself or by others who observe him. When the person himself gains this evidence, he receives conviction of sin, especially that conviction concerning the defilement of his nature and the sin of unbelief, for the sake of which he is certain to be damned unless he finds mercy at *God's* hand through faith in *Jesus Christ*.[30] This perspective and sensibility produces in him sorrow and shame for sin; moreover, he finds the *Savior* of the world revealed to him, and the absolute necessity of his closing with him for life, in which case he discovers a hunger and thirst for him, he to whom indeed the promise has been made.[31]

Now according to the strength or weakness of his faith in his *Savior*, so is his joy and peace, so is his love for holiness, so are his desires to know him more, and also to serve him in this world. But though I explain that this is a revelation unto himself; yet it is seldom that he is able to conclude that this is a work of grace, because his present corruptions and his abused reason cause his mind to misjudge in this matter. Therefore, in he who has such an inward work, there is required very sound judgment before he can confidently conclude that this is a work of grace.

To others this work of grace is externally evidenced as follows. First, by a confession of faith in *Christ* born of genuine experience. Second, by a life that is in agreement with such a confession, that is a life of holiness, specifically heart holiness, family holiness (if he has a family), and by daily behavior holiness in the world.[32]

So this holiness in general inwardly teaches him to abhor his sin and himself in the privacy of his heart; to suppress his sin in family life; and to promote holiness in the world. This he does, not by talk alone as the hypocrite or talkative person is

---

30 Mark 16:16; John 16:8-9; Rom. 7:24.

31 Ps. 38:18; Jer. 31:19; Matt. 5:6; Acts 4:12; Gal. 2:15-16; Rev. 21:6.

32 *Ps. 50:23; Eccles. 12:13; Matt. 5:8; John 14:15; Rom. 10:9-10; Phil. 1:27; 3:17-20; I Pet. 2:11-12.*

accustomed to do, but by a practical subjection, through faith and love, to the power of the *Word*.[33] And now Sir, concerning this brief description of the work of grace and its evidence in true religion, if you have any objections to what I have said, then do declare them right now. But if not, then allow me to propose to you a second question.

TALKATIVE: No, I have nothing more to say; it seems pointless to object; rather let me hear. So what is your second question?

FAITHFUL: It is this. Do you personally experience the first part of my description of a true work of grace? And do your life and daily behavior testify to this same experience? Or is your religion based solely upon word and speech, exclusive of deed and truth?[34] By all means respond if you feel inclined to do so; but only speak that which you know the *God* of *Heaven* will accept as true, as well as that which your conscience can justify. For not he who commends himself is in reality approved, but he whom the Lord commends.[35] Besides, to say that I am such and such, when my daily behavior and neighbors plainly testify that I lie, surely this is great wickedness.

TALKATIVE: (Beginning to blush, though recovering) You now focus upon experience and conscience and *God*, as well as appeals to Him for justification of what you say. I did not expect this kind of conversation, nor am I inclined to give an answer to such questions because I do not feel obliged to do so, that is unless you have appointed yourself as my catechizer [*examiner*]; and even if you had, I would probably refuse to have you as my judge. But I do long to know why you have asked me such questions.

FAITHFUL: Because I noticed your eagerness to talk while having no reason to believe that this was any more than notion [*speculation*]. Besides, to be very truthful with you, I have heard that by reputation you are a man whose religion is based upon

---

[33] Job 42:5-6; Ps. 50:23; Ezek. 20:43; Matt. 5:9; John 14:15; Rom. 10:9-10; Phil. 1:27; *3:17-20*.

[34] *I John 3:18*.

[35] *II Cor. 10:18*.

pure talk, and that your daily behavior betrays the hypocrisy of your mouth-profession.

They say you are a stain in the midst of Christians, and that true religion suffers on account of your ungodly lifestyle, that some have already stumbled because of your wicked ways, and that more are in danger of making shipwreck of their faith.[36] Your religion involves fellowship with tavern life and covetousness and uncleanness and swearing and lying and worldly company and more. The proverb that describes a prostitute is also descriptive of you; in that she is a shame to women, so you are similarly a shame to all genuine Christians.

TALKATIVE: Since you are quick to listen to reports about me, and to judge so rashly, I cannot but conclude that you are some irritable or mournful fellow who is not worthy of being conversed with, and so adieu [*farewell*].[37]

CHRISTIAN: (Having approached his companion) Did I not tell you how this encounter would end? Your words and *Talkative's* lusts could not agree. He preferred to leave your company rather than reform his life. But as I said, he is gone; so let him go. This loss belongs to none other than himself, and he has saved us the trouble of our departing from him. And assuming that he will continue as he is, he would only have been a stain on our company. Besides, the apostle says, "From such withdraw yourself."[38]

FAITHFUL: But I am glad that we had this short discussion with him; it may happen that he will further think about it. However, I have spoken plainly with him so that if he perishes, I am innocent of his blood.[39]

CHRISTIAN: You did well to speak so frankly to him as you did; there is little of this faithful dealing with men today, and it is for this reason that true religion is so understandably odorous in the nostrils of many. For there are these talkative fools whose religion is only in word; they are morally corrupt and vain in

---

36 *I Tim. 1:19; Jude 12-16.*

37 *Amos 3:3; Gal. 6:14; I John 2:19.*

38 *I Tim. 6:5.*

39 *Acts 20:26; Ezek. 33:1-9.*

their conversation, and on being so numerously admitted into the fellowship of the godly, do confuse the world, blemish Christianity, and grieve the sincere. I wish that all men would deal with these imposters as you have done; then they would either be made more agreeable to true religion, or else the fellowship of true pilgrims would prove to be too hot for them.

Then did *Faithful* say:

> How *Talkative* at first lifts up his plumes!
> How bravely does he speak! How he presumes
> To drive down all before him! But so soon
> As *Faithful* talks of heartwork,[40] like the moon
> That's past the full, into the wane he goes;
> And so will all, but he that heartwork knows.

Talkative

---

[40] *"Heartwork" describes the sanctifying life of God in the soul of the genuine pilgrim as distinct from confessional and orthodox hypocrites such as Talkative.*

20

EVANGELIST REAPPEARS TO GIVE TIMELY WARNING

THUS they went on talking about what they had seen along the way, and this discussion made their travel easier, otherwise their journeying would undoubtedly have been tedious, for now they passed through a *Wilderness*.

Now when they had almost passed out of this *Wilderness*, *Faithful* happened to look behind and on doing so he noticed someone coming after them, who he suddenly recognized. "Oh!" said *Faithful* to his brother. "Who is it that approaches us from behind?" Then *Christian* looked and exclaimed, "It is my good friend *Evangelist*." "Yes, and my good friend as well," said *Faithful,* "for it was he who directed me along the way that leads to the *Wicket-gate*." Then did *Evangelist* reach them and offer his greeting.

EVANGELIST: Peace be with you, dearly beloved, and may there be peace upon those who have helped you.

CHRISTIAN: Welcome, welcome, my good *Evangelist*; the sight of your face reminds me of your earlier kindness as well as your untiring labor for my eternal good.

FAITHFUL: And let me add a thousand welcomes. Oh sweet *Evangelist*, how desirable is your fellowship to us who are such needy pilgrims.

EVANGELIST: How have you managed, my friends, since the time of our last meeting? What have you encountered, and how have you behaved yourselves?

Then *Christian* and *Faithful* told him of all the things that had happened to them along the way, and how they had passed through many difficulties up to this point in their journey.

EVANGELIST: How glad I am, not so much that you met with trials, but rather that you have proved to be victors over them. And for this reason you have been enabled to continue thus far, notwithstanding your many weaknesses.[1]

---

1 *Acts 26:22.*

Again I say just how pleased I am of this matter, and that for my own sake as well as yours. I have sowed, and you have reaped, and the day is coming when both he that sowed and they that reaped shall rejoice together, that is if you hold out [*to the end*]. For in due time you shall reap if you do not faint.[2] The crown [*of reward*] is before you, and it is an incorruptible one; so run that you may obtain it.[3] There are some that have set out for this crown, and after they have traveled a great distance, another steps in and takes it from them. Therefore hold fast what you have and do not let any man take away your crown; you are not yet beyond the gunshot of the *Devil*; you have not resisted unto blood, striving against sin. So always let the kingdom be before you, and steadfastly believe concerning the things that are invisible.[4] Let nothing in this life come between yourself and the world to come.

Above all, pay attention to your own hearts with their indwelling lusts, for they are deceitful above all things and desperately wicked. Set your face with flint-like resolve since you have all power in *Heaven* and *Earth* on your side.[5]

Then *Christian* thanked him for his exhortation, but added that they would prefer that he speak some more, that is something helpful about the rest of the way ahead. Since they knew that he was a prophet, they were anxious to know about the things that might happen to them, and also how they might resist and overcome them. So *Evangelist* agreed to speak further.

EVANGELIST: My sons, you have heard in the words of the truth of the gospel that you must enter the kingdom of *Heaven* through many tribulations.[6] And again you have heard that imprisonment and afflictions will accompany you.[7] And therefore you cannot expect that you should travel far on your pilgrimage without encountering them in one way or another.

---

[2] John 4:36-37; Gal. 6:9.

[3] I Cor. 9:24-27; *Phil. 3:13-14*; Rev. 3:11.

[4] *II Cor. 4:18; Heb. 11:27; 12:4.*

[5] *Isa. 50:7; Jer. 17:9; Matt. 28:18; Luke 9:51.*

[6] *Acts 14:22.*

[7] *Acts 20:23.*

You have already experienced a measure of the truth of this testimony, and more will immediately follow.

For now, as you see, you are almost out of this *Wilderness*, and therefore you will eventually come to a *Town* that will appear directly in front of you. Now in that *Town* you will be severely assaulted by enemies who will make every attempt to kill you. Now you may be sure that one or both of you will seal the testimony which you profess with blood.[8] Nevertheless, be faithful unto death and the *King* will give you a crown of life.[9]

Whoever shall die there, although his death will be unnatural and his pain probably great, yet he will have the advantage over his companion; this will be, not only because he will arrive at the *Celestial City* sooner, but also because he will escape the many miseries that the other will meet with in the rest of his journey. But when you have come to this *Town*, and all that I have spoken about has been fulfilled, then remember your friend and quit [*behave*] yourselves as men; and commit the keeping of your souls to your *God*, as unto a faithful *Creator*.[10]

Justice Lord Hategood

---

8 *John 21:18-19.*

9 *Rev. 2:10.*

10 *I Pet. 4:19.*

21
CHRISTIAN AND FAITHFUL ON TRIAL AT VANITY FAIR

THEN I saw in my dream that when *Christian* and *Faithful* had come out of the *Wilderness*, they immediately saw ahead of them a *Town* which was named *Vanity*. Now at this *Town*, a fair is promoted there that is known as *Vanity Fair*. It is maintained all the year long and bears the name *Vanity Fair* because the *Town* where it is located is regarded as lighter than vanity; and also, because all that is sold there, as well as those who come to buy, is vanity [*worthless*]. As is the saying of the wise man, "All that this world promotes is vanity."[1]

This *Fair* is not some newly constructed business, but an enterprise going back into antiquity. Let me tell you about its origin. Almost five thousand years ago, even then there were pilgrims walking toward the *Celestial City*, just as these two honest persons are doing. So *Beelzebub*, *Apollyon*, and *Legion*,[2] along with their associates, noticing that the path along which pilgrims traveled toward the *City* passed through this *Town of Vanity*, they determined to construct a fair;[3] it was to be a festive market in which there would be sold every sort of vanity, and it would be open all the year long. Therefore at this *Fair* every type of merchandise was sold, including houses, lands, trades, places, honors, promotions, titles, countries, kingdoms, lusts, and pleasures; there were also delights of all sorts such as prostitutes, madams, wives, husbands, children, masters, servants, lives, blood, bodies, souls, silver, gold, pearls, precious stones, and much more.[4]

And moreover, at this *Fair* there is the constant entertainment of jugglers, cheats, games, plays, clowns, mimics, tricksters, rogues, and many other amusements. Here also are to

---

1 *Ps. 62:9;* Eccles. 1:2, 12-18; 2:1-26; *11:8*; Isa. 40:17.

2 *Mark 5:9.*

3 *II Cor. 4:4.*

4 *Matt. 6:31-32; Rev. 18:11-14.*

be found a number of free offerings including thefts, murders, adulteries, perjurers, all available in various shades of blood [*scarlet*].[5] And as in other fairs of lesser importance, there are several lanes and streets with representative names where certain categories of merchandise are marketed; so here it is the same, for you have places, lanes, and streets named after countries and kingdoms where the goods of this *Fair* are to be found. There is the *Britain Row*, the *French Row*, the *Italian Row*, the *Spanish Row*, the *German Row*, where a variety of vanities is sold.

But as in other fairs, where one commodity group tends to dominate over all others, so the merchandise of *Rome* is lavishly promoted in this *Fair*. However, our English nation, along with some others, has expressed a disliking for this flaunted huckstering.[6] Now as I said, the way to the *Celestial City* runs directly through this *Town* with its lusty *Fair*; and he who would go to that *City*, and yet not pass through this *Town*, must necessarily go out of the world.[7]

The *Prince of Princes* himself, when traveling in this region, passed through this *Town* when heading toward his own country, and at a time when the *Fair* was in full operation. Yes, and I believe is was *Beelzebub*, the chief *Lord* of this *Fair*, who personally invited him to buy some of his vanities; yes, he would have even made him a *Lord* of this *Fair* if only the *Prince* had bowed to his overall authority while passing through the *Town*. Further, because he was such a person of honor, *Beelzebub* escorted him from street to street and showed him, in a short space of time, all the kingdoms of the world so that he might lure the *Blessed One* to lower himself and buy some of his vanities. But this *Stranger* had no desire whatsoever for this merchandise, and therefore he departed from the *Town* without spending so much as one cent on these worthless goods.[8]

---

5 *Rev. 17:3-4; 18:11-14.*

6 *This is evidenced by the English Reformation facilitated by King Henry VIII in 1534, and the defeat of the Spanish Armada by Queen Elizabeth I in 1588.*

7 *John 17:14-17*; I Cor. 5:9-10.

8 Matt. 4:8-10; Luke 4:5-8; *Heb. 12:3.*

Therefore, this *Fair* is certainly an antiquity of long standing, and a very great *Fair* at that.

Now as I said, these pilgrims must necessarily pass through this *Fair*. Well, so they did; but especially note that even as they entered the *Fair*, all of the people there became disturbed, and the whole *Town* itself was turned into a commotion around them. There were several reasons for this, namely:

First, the pilgrims were dressed with a type of clothing that was quite different from the attire of those who traded at that *Fair*.[9] Therefore the people of the *Fair* stared at them with astonishment. Some of them said that they were fools, and some called them bedlams [*madmen*], while others derided them as outlandish men [*foreigners*].[10]

Second, as the great crowd wondered at their clothing, so they were similarly curious about their speech, for few could understand what they said. The pilgrims spoke their native tongue, the language of *Canaan*;[11] but those who managed and frequented the *Fair* were the men who spoke the language of this world. So that throughout the *Fair* their foreign speaking made them appear as barbarians in their midst.[12]

Third, and this did especially amuse the merchants, these pilgrims placed little value on all of their goods; they did not even care to browse at them; and if they were solicited to buy such items, they would put their fingers in their ears and cry out, "Turn away my eyes from beholding vanity;"[13] at the same time they would look upward signifying that their trade and commerce were with *Heaven*.

So beholding the strange behavior of these men, one scornful trader happened to address them: "What will you buy?" But the pilgrims soberly replied, "We buy the truth."[14] At this, opportunity was taken all the more to pour contempt upon these men.

---

[9] *Isa. 61:10; Gal. 3:27; Phil. 3:8-9.*

[10] *Job 12:4; I Cor. 4:9-10.*

[11] *Isa. 19:18*; I Cor. 2:6-8; *I John 4:5-6.*

[12] *I Cor. 2:7-8; 14:11.*

[13] Ps. 119:37; Phil. 3:19-20; *I John 2:15-17.*

[14] Prov. 23:23; *John 17:17.*

Some mocked, some taunted, some spoke reproachfully, and some called upon others to strike them. Eventually things came to a great commotion and disturbance in the *Fair*, so much so that disorder was everywhere.[15] As a result, word was brought to the governor of the *Fair* who quickly came down and appointed deputies, some of his most trusted friends, to examine these pilgrims concerning why they had brought about this disturbance of the *Fair*.

So the men were taken aside for investigation; and those who presided at this enquiry asked them from where they came, and where they were going, and why they were so unusually dressed. *Christian* and *Faithful* told them that they were pilgrims and strangers in this world, and that they were traveling to their own country, which is called the *Heavenly Jerusalem*,[16] and that they had not given any cause for the men of the *Town* or the merchants to abuse them, and to delay them in their journey. The only possible exception could be that when asked to buy some goods there, they responded that they would only buy the truth.

But the appointed examiners did not believe them, though they did regard them as madmen and lunatics, and likely to be the sort who would bring confusion to the *Fair*. Therefore they were detained to be beaten, then besmeared with dirt and caged in such a way as to be made a spectacle to all the men of the *Fair*.[17] And there they lay for some time while being made the objects of any man's sport or malice or revenge. Meanwhile, the governor of the *Fair* only continued to laugh at their plight.

But the pilgrims remained patient and never returned abuse for abuse received; on the contrary, they only blessed while speaking good words for bad, and acted kindly in the face of brutal treatment.[18] However, some men at the *Fair*, who were more discerning and less prejudiced than most, began to restrain the more degraded types and accuse them of continual abuse of

---

[15] *Ps. 2:1-3; Acts 19:23-41.*

[16] Heb. 11:13-16; *I Pet. 1:1; 2:11.*

[17] *I Cor. 4:9, 13.*

[18] *Rom. 12:17-21; I Thess. 2:1-12; I Pet. 3:9.*

the captives.[19] In response, these baser sort let fly at there challengers and began to regard them as bad as the caged pilgrims; they accused them of being accomplices and worthy of receiving the same mistreatment. The others then replied that as far as they could see, the two transients were quiet, sober, and harmless in nature; further they regarded many who attended the *Fair* as being much more worthy of being caged, yes, and pilloried as well, than the men presently being assailed. So after an exchange of a variety of opinions on both sides, while at the same time the pilgrims themselves behaved both wisely and soberly, the opposing groups began to physically assault and injure each other.

Then the two prisoners were again brought before their examiners and charged with being guilty of causing the recent disturbance at the *Fair*. As a result they beat them unmercifully, hung them in irons, and paraded them in chains up and down the streets of the *Fair*; this being intended to make them an example and warning to the citizens lest any should be tempted to defend the pilgrims or associate themselves with the them. But *Christian* and *Faithful* behaved themselves with increasing wisdom while continuing to have humiliation and shame cast upon them; yet with so much meekness and patience, they did begin to win to their side a comparative few of the men at the *Fair*. This caused the more militant opponents to only rage all the more, so much so that they now sought the death penalty for the prisoners. Therefore they announced that not merely the cage and irons were sufficient to satisfy them, but that the strangers should die on account of the damage they had caused and the deception of some of the men of the *Fair*.[20]

Then *Christian* and *Faithful* were remanded to the cage again until the process of law could deal with them. Here they were incarcerated with their feet fastened in the stocks.[21] Here also they recalled to mind what they had formerly heard from their faithful friend *Evangelist*; this caused them to be confirmed in

---

[19] *Acts 17:7.*

[20] *John 3:19.*

[21] *Acts 16:24.*

their acceptance of the conditions and trials of the way since they had been told about them before they actually occurred. Now they also comforted each other by reasoning that whoever was chosen to suffer [*unto death*], he would indeed have the advantage. Therefore each man secretly desired that he might have the preference here; yet they both committed themselves to the all-wise and sovereign purposes of the *Almighty*; so being full of content, they rested in the condition in which they found themselves waiting to see how they would be disposed of.

When a convenient time had been determined, the prisoners were brought forth to be tried in order that they might be found guilty and condemned. So that time having come, they were brought before their enemies to be formally accused; the name of the appointed judge was *Lord Hate-good*. The accusation was essentially the same as what had already been declared, though it included some minor variation. The contents were as follows:

"That they [*Christian and Faithful*] were enemies of, and disturbers of the trading at the *Fair*; that they had caused both commotions and divisions in the *Town*, and had gained supporters for their most dangerous opinions, in contempt of the law of their *Prince* [*Beelzebub*]."[22]

Then *Faithful* gave his answer, explaining that he had only spoken against that which had asserted itself against the *Highest*. He further said, "As for causing a disturbance, I made none since I am a man of peace; the party that began to support us were persuaded through their recognition of our truth and innocence, and thus they turned from a worse condition to a better. And as for the king that you talk about, since he is *Beelzebub*, the enemy of our *Lord*, I defy him and all his hellish angels."[23]

Then it was proclaimed that those who had anything to say in support of their *Lord* the *King* against the prisoner at the bar should immediately appear to so testify. So there came forward three witnesses, namely *Envy*,[24] *Superstition* [*formal*

---

22 *Acts 19:25. There is also a reflection here of Bunyan's indictment in 1661 as a "disturbance and great distraction."*

23 *Acts 5:29; 6:8-7:60..*

24 *Matt. 27:18.*

religion, popery], and *Pickthank* [*a self-serving tell-tale*]. They were then asked if they knew the prisoner at the bar, and what they had to say in support of their *Lord* the *King* against him. *Envy* was first to testify, and he spoke this way, "My *Lord*, I have known this man a long time, and will attest under oath before this honorable bench that he is —"

JUDGE: Hold on a moment; first administer the oath to him.

So he was sworn in to tell the truth.

Then *Envy* continued, "My *Lord*, this man, in spite of his plausible name, is one of the vilest men in our country; he regards neither our *Prince* nor his people, laws, or customs; rather he does all that he can to persuade the men of our *Town* concerning his subversive ideas, which in general he declares to be principles of faith and holiness.[25] And in particular, I myself once heard him assert that *Christianity* and the customs of our *Town of Vanity* were diametrically opposite, and could not be reconciled. Now, my *Lord*, by this statement he not only condemns all of our praiseworthy good works, but also ourselves in our doing of them."

JUDGE: Have you anything more to say?

ENVY: My *Lord*, I could say a great deal more, only I would not weary the court with this detail. Yet, if it is necessary, when the other gentlemen have given their evidence, to avoid any lack of testimony that might allow the prisoner to go free, I would be willing to declare further evidence.

So the *Judge* requested that he remain at the trial in case his further testimony was needed. Following this *Superstition* was called to the stand and told to look toward the prisoner; then he was also asked what he could say in defense of their *Lord* the *King* against him. Having been sworn in, then he commenced to testify.

SUPERSTITION: My *Lord*, I have had no great acquaintance with this man, nor do I desire to have any further knowledge of him. However, this I do know, that he is a very pestilent [*troublesome*] fellow,[26] and from some discussion that I had with him in this *Town* the other day, I distinctly heard him declare

---

[25] *Acts 16:20-21; 17:7.*

[26] *Acts 24:5.*

that our religion was vain, and it was of the type by which it would be impossible for a man to please *God*. Now, my *Lordship*, you very well know what conclusively follows from such sayings; it is that we are presently continuing in this vain worship and as a result remain in our sins, and finally shall be damned. So this is what I have to say.

Then was *Pickthank* sworn in, and he was also asked what he knew, in support of their *Lord* the *King*, against the prisoner at the bar.

PICKTHANK: My *Lord*, and all of your gentlemen, I have known this fellow for a long time and heard him speak of things that ought not to be spoken. For he has denounced our noble *Prince Beelzebub*, and spoken contemptuously of his honorable friends, whose names are the *Lord Old Man*, the *Lord Carnal Delight*, the *Lord Luxurious*, the *Lord Desire of Vain-glory*, my old *Lord Lechery* [*Lusty*], *Sir Having Greedy*, with all of the rest of our nobility.[27] Moreover, he has said that if it were possible for all men to be of his opinion, then not one of these noblemen would anymore reside in this *Town*. Besides, he has not been afraid of reviling even you, my *Lord*, who are now appointed to be his judge; he has called you an ungodly villain, along with many other slanderous names; most of the gentry of our *Town* have been similarly smeared.

Thus when this *Pickthank* had concluded giving his evidence, the *Judge* directed his speech toward the prisoner at the bar, saying, "You deserter of the truth, you heretic and traitor; have you heard what these honest gentlemen have testified against you?"

FAITHFUL: May I speak a few words in my own defense?[28]

JUDGE: You contemptible fellow! You good-for-nothing vagrant! You do not deserve to live any longer, but rather to be immediately put to death here and now. Yet so that all men may recognize our gentleness toward you, let us hear what you have to say.[29]

---

27 Sins are all Lords, and great ones.

28 *Acts 22:1.*

29 *Acts 22:22.*

FAITHFUL: First, in reply to what *Mr. Envy* has declared, I never said anything except that whatever rules or laws or customs or people are plainly opposed to the *Word of God*, they are also diametrically opposite to *Christianity*. If anything that I have said in this regard is incorrect, then do persuade me of my error; I am more than willing to renounce my folly, if you can clearly prove it.[30]

Second, as to the charge that *Mr. Superstition* brought against me, I can only say this, that in the true worship of *God* a divine faith is required; but there can be no divine faith without a divine revelation of the will of *God*. Therefore, whatever is employed in the worship of *God*, that is not in agreement with divine revelation, cannot be sourced in anything else than human faith, which faith will not result in eternal life.[31]

Third, concerning what *Mr. Pickthank* had to say, while avoiding those abusive terms that I have been accused of using, nevertheless I say that the *Prince* of this *Town*, and all of the attending rabble that he has appointed, are more fit for being in *Hell* than in this *Town* and country; and so may the *Lord* have mercy upon me.

Then the *Judge* addressed the jury who all this while had been watching and listening nearby. "Gentlemen of the jury, you see this man who has been the center of a violent controversy in this *Town*;[32] you have also heard what these worthy gentlemen have testified against him; furthermore you have listened to his reply and confession. It now rests in your heartfelt decision as to whether he should live or die. Nevertheless, I believe it is proper that I should instruct you about the precedents of our law."

"In the days of *Pharaoh the Great*, a servant of our *Prince*, there was an act made that addressed the danger of those who would promote false religion and cause it to multiply in our midst and thus overcome the whole realm. So it was decreed that the males of such false prophets should be thrown into the river.[33] There was another act made in the days of *King*

---

[30] *John 18:23; Acts 25:11.*

[31] *The Puritan regulative principle concerning right worship.*

[32] *Acts 19:28-41.*

[33] Exod. 1:8-22.

Nebuchadnezzar the Great, also a servant of our *Prince*; it declared that whoever would not fall down and worship his golden image should be thrown into a fiery furnace."[34]

"Yet another act was established in the days of *King Darius*, that whoever, for an appointed period of time, would call upon any other god than he himself should be cast into the lions' den.[35] Now this rebel has broken the substance of these laws, not only in thought, which is not an indictable offence, but also in word and deed; therefore these actions cannot be tolerated."

"Concerning the law of *Pharaoh*, it was promulgated for the purpose of preventing trouble before it had actually happened. But in this instance, an actual crime is all too apparent. With regard to the second and third precedents, you will notice how the prisoner also argues against our religion in much the same way. Therefore on account of the treason which he has openly confessed to, he deserves to die as a criminal."

Then the jury, whose names were *Mr. Blind-man*, *Mr. No-good*, *Mr. Malice*, *Mr. Love-lust*, *Mr. Live-loose*, *Mr. Heady*, *Mr. High-mind*, *Mr. Enmity*, *Mr. Liar*, *Mr. Cruelty*, *Mr. Hate-light*, and *Mr. Implacable*, retired to consider a verdict.[36] In consultation amongst themselves, each individual concluded that the prisoner was guilty, and so their verdict proved to be unanimous; for each jury member had voiced his condemnation. First, the foreman of the jury, *Mr. Blind-man* said, "I clearly see that this man is a heretic." Then *Mr. No-good* said, "Let us be rid of such a fellow from the face of the *Earth*."[37] "Yes," said *Mr. Malice*, "for I hate the very appearance of this man."

Then *Mr. Love-lust* said, "I could never tolerate him." "Nor could I," responded *Mr. Live-loose*, "for he would always be condemning my lifestyle." "Hang him, hang him," said *Mr. Heady*. "He is a sorry scrub [*ruffian*]," said *Mr. High-mind*. "My heart boils with anger against him," said *Mr. Enmity*. "He is a rogue," said *Mr. Liar*. "Hanging is too good for him," said *Mr. Cruelty*. "Let us dispose of him immediately," said *Mr. Hate-*

---

[34] Dan. 3:1-30.

[35] Dan. 6:1-28.

[36] *II Tim. 3:1-4.*

[37] *Acts 22:22.*

light. Then *Mr. Implacable* said, "If I would be given the whole world, still I could not be reconciled to him; therefore, let us deliver our verdict and find him guilty of death." So the *Judge*, having been advised of the jury's agreement, delivered his sentence. *Faithful* was condemned to be returned to his prison cell, and there to be put to death by means of the most cruel method possible.

Therefore they brought the condemned prisoner out to execute him according to their law. First they scourged him, then they severely mauled [*battered*] him, after this they slashed his flesh with knives; further they stoned him and lanced him with their swords, and finally they burned him to ashes at the stake.[38] So *Faithful* came to his earthly end. Now I noticed that behind the watching multitude there stood a chariot and a pair of horses waiting for *Faithful*; for as soon as his adversaries had executed him, he was immediately placed in it and transported up through the clouds, with trumpet accompaniment, by means of the shortest route, to the gate of the *Celestial City*.[39]

But as for *Christian*, he had some relief in the midst of this agonizing situation in his being remanded back to prison. So there he remained for a period of time. Nevertheless, he that overrules all things, having the power of their rage in the palm of his hand,[40] ordered events in such a way that *Christian* was enabled, on that occasion, to escape from the *Town* and continue on his way.

And as he went along, he sang:

> Well *Faithful*, you have faithfully professed
> Unto your *Lord*: with him you will be blessed;
> When faithless ones, with all their vain delights,
> Are crying out under their hellish plights.
> Sing, *Faithful*, sing; and let your name survive;
> For though they killed you, yet you are alive.[41]

---

[38] *Matt. 26:67; 27:26; John 18:31; 19:7; Heb. 11:36-38. There is also allusion here to Foxe's Book of Martyrs.*

[39] *II Kings 2:11.*

[40] *Ps. 76:10.*

[41] *Rev. 14:13.*

22
CHRISTIAN AND HOPEFUL CONVERSE WITH BY-ENDS

NOW I saw in my dream that *Christian* did not press on alone, for another pilgrim named *Hopeful* joined with him and, by means of a brotherly covenant, agreed to be his companion. He was persuaded to take this course because of the witness of *Christian* and *Faithful*, and especially their suffering, at *Vanity Fair*. Thus one died to make a testimony to the truth, and another arose from his ashes to become a companion for *Christian*. This *Hopeful* also told *Christian* that there were many more men at the *Fair* who would, after a while, follow him.

So I noticed that soon after they had departed from the *Fair*, they overtook another pilgrim ahead of them whose name was *By-ends*.[1] So they said to him, "Sir, what country are you from? And how far are you going in this direction?" He told them that he came from the *Town of Fair-speech*, and that he was going to the *Celestial City*, though he did not mention his name.

CHRISTIAN: You say you come from *Fair-speech*?[2] Do any good and commendable people live there?

BY-ENDS: Yes, I hope so.

CHRISTIAN: Then sir, do tell me by what name I may call you.

BY-ENDS: I am a stranger to you even as you are to me; if you are going my way, then I shall be glad to have your company; but if not, I will have to be content.

CHRISTIAN: I have heard of this *Town of Fair-speech*, and from what I can remember, it is said to be a wealthy place.

BY-ENDS: Yes, I can assure you that it is, and I have many rich friends there.

CHRISTIAN: Then if I may be so bold, do tell me who some of these friends are.

---

1 *A religious man with ulterior motives. His external piety conceals internal duplicity.*

2 Prov. 26:24-25; *Rom. 16:18.*

BY-ENDS: To be honest, almost the whole *Town*, and in particular, my *Lord Turn-about*, my *Lord Time-server*, my *Lord Fair-speech* (from whose ancestors the *Town* first took its name). Also there is *Mr. Smooth-man*, *Mr. Facing-both-ways*, *Mr. Anything*, and the parson of our parish, *Mr. Two-tongues*,[3] who was my mother's own brother on my father's side.[4] And to tell you the truth, I have become a gentleman of high quality; though my great-grandfather was merely an oarsman for hire who would look one way and row another;[5] I obtained most of my possessions by means of the same occupation.

CHRISTIAN: Are you a married man?

BY-ENDS: Yes, and my wife is a very virtuous woman. She was my *Lady Feigning's* [*Pretender's*] daughter, and therefore she came from a very honorable family; as a result she has reached a high level of breeding; her deportment is always impeccable before either princes or peasants. It is true that our religion differs to some degree when compared with that more strict variety, but only in two small points. First, we never strive against the wind and the tide. Second, we are always very zealous in following religion that parades in silver slippers; we love to walk with such sumptuous company, that is when the sun shines and people applaud.

Then *Christian* stepped a little to one side to his companion *Hopeful* and commented, "It comes to my mind that this fellow is in fact *By-ends* of *Fair-speech*, and if this is true, we have quite a scoundrel here, the like of which is often found in these parts." So *Hopeful* suggested, "Then you should ask him to be sure; I would think that he ought not to be ashamed of his name."

Hence *Christian* approached him to make this enquiry.

CHRISTIAN: Sir, you talk as if you knew more than the whole world, and if I am not mistaken, with only half a guess you are easily identified. Is not your name *Mr. By-ends* of *Fair-speech*?

BY-ENDS: That is not my name, though it is a nickname that has been attributed to me by those who cannot suffer me; but I

---

[3] *I Tim. 3:8.*

[4] *A suitable conundrum.*

[5] *Matthew Henry uses this proverb in his commentary on Isa. 33:15.*

must be content to endure this reproach, just as other good men have done when similarly maligned.

CHRISTIAN: But were you ever responsible for a situation where men could have rightly called you by this name?

BY-ENDS: Never, never! The worst circumstance that might have caused some to call me by this name was when I always had the luck in my judgment to jump in a profitable direction, in harmony with the present movement of the times. But if I am criticized for these events, then let me regard them as a blessing rather than bear a load of hatred against my critics.

CHRISTIAN: But I was so sure that you were this man that I had heard about, and to be honest, I fear that his name is more appropriate for you than you might want us to believe.

BY-ENDS: Well, you can imagine what you like; I cannot help that. Though you will find me a reasonably minded companion, that is if you allow me to travel with you.

CHRISTIAN: If you would walk with us, then you must go against wind and tide, which, as I understand it, is contrary to your convictions. You must also welcome religion in its rags as well as when it wears silver slippers, and accompany pilgrims bound in shackles as well as when they walk the streets and are applauded.

BY-ENDS: But you ought not to impose this upon me, nor coerce my faith;[6] rather, respect my liberty and allow me to travel with you.

CHRISTIAN: No, not a step further will you go with us unless you agree with our standards of fellowship.

BY-ENDS: I shall never desert my long-standing principles since they are harmless and profitable. If you will not let me walk with you, I must continue as I did before we met and travel alone, that is until someone else overtakes me and appreciates my company.

Now I saw in my dream that *Christian* and *Hopeful* moved ahead of *By-ends* so as to be separate from him; but one of them looked back and noticed three men following after *Mr. By-ends.* So they caught up with him, and he, having made a very low *Conje* [*bow of address*] toward them, received a friendly

---

[6] *II Cor. 1:24.*

welcome in return. The names of these men were *Mr. Hold-the-world*, *Mr. Money-love*, and *Mr. Save-all*, men that *Mr. By-ends* had formerly been acquainted with; for in their youth they were all school chums and had been taught by their schoolmaster *Mr. Gripe-man*, in *Love-gain*, a market town in *Coveting County* in the north.[7] This schoolmaster taught them the art of acquisition, either by means of violence, cozenage [*cheating*], flattery, lying, or using the guise [*masquerade*] of religion;[8] and all four of these gentlemen attained such a great degree of the skill of their master that any of them could themselves have maintained a similar school.

Well, as I said, when they had finished greeting one another, *Mr. Money-love* said to *Mr. By-ends*, "Who are they who are walking on the road ahead of us?" For *Christian* and *Hopeful* were still within view.

BY-ENDS: They are a couple of distant countrymen who, according to their own perspective, are going on pilgrimage.

MONEY-LOVE: How unfortunate; why did they not wait so that we might join their good company, for sir, I hope that they and we and you are all going on pilgrimage.

BY-ENDS: Indeed we are, but the men ahead of us are so rigid and so in love with their ideas, and they so lightly value the opinions of others that, be there a man ever so godly, yet if he does not jump with them in all things, they immediately thrust him away from their company.

SAVE-ALL: That is bad. But we read of some that are excessively righteous, and this rigidity of such men constrains them to judge and condemn everyone except themselves.[9] But do tell me, what were these things in which you differed? And how many of them were there?

BY-ENDS: Why, according to their headstrong manner, they believe it to be their duty to rush ahead on their journey in all types of weather, while I am for waiting for the right wind and

---

7 *An area of savage, predatory evil. Jer. 4:6; 6:22-23; 10:22.*

8 *I Thess. 2:1-6.*

9 *Puritans were charged with being "precisians," that is morally precise and extremely scrupulous. Eccles. 7:16.*

tide. They are for risking all for *God*,[10] and in an instant I would grasp advantages that secure my life and property. They are for holding on to their beliefs even though all other men oppose them; but I am for religion that is tolerant of the times and not a threat to my safety. They are for religion when it dresses in rags and is regarded as contemptible, but I am for religious company that walks in golden slippers in the sunshine while observers applaud.

HOLD THE WORLD: Yes, and hold it there, my good *Mr. By-ends*. For my part, I can only count him a fool who, having the liberty to keep what he has, shall be so unwise as to lose it.[11] Rather let us be wise as serpents;[12] it is best to make hay while the sun shines; you notice how the bee rests all winter long and stirs herself only when it is profitable and pleasurable to do so. Sometimes *God* sends rain and sometimes sunshine; if they be so foolish as to go through the first, still let us be content to take the fair weather as our portion.[13]

For my part, the religion I like best is that which enjoys the security of *God's* good blessings poured out on us. For the thoughtful person it stands to reason that if *God* has given us the good things of this life, then he would have us continue to enjoy them in this life for his sake.[14] *Abraham* and *Solomon* grew rich through religion. And *Job* declares that a good man shall store up gold as dust.[15] This being so, he could not be like the men ahead of us as you have described them.

SAVE-ALL: I think that we are all agreed about this matter, and therefore no more needs to be said about it.

MONEY-LOVE: As you say, nothing more needs to be said at this point; for he who believes neither Scripture nor reason, and you see that we have both of these witnesses in our support, does not appreciate his own liberty or care for his own safety.

---

[10] *Acts 15:26.*

[11] *Matt. 16:25.*

[12] *Gen. 3:1; Matt. 10:16.*

[13] *Here is a montage of secular proverb and various emblems.*

[14] *Acts 14:17; I Tim. 6:17.*

[15] *A misunderstanding of Job 22:24.*

BY-ENDS: My brothers, as you can see, we are all going on pilgrimage, so to divert our attention from things that are bad, do allow me to propose to you this question. Suppose a man, who is a minister of religion or a tradesman or someone else, should have a possible promotion come to his attention by means of which he could obtain the good blessings of this life; yet he can only gain this advantage through appearing very zealous in certain points of religion that he had previously neglected; should he not use this religious means so as to attain his end, while remaining a perfectly honest man?

MONEY-LOVE: I understand the substance of your question, and with the ready permission of these gentlemen, I will attempt to provide an answer. First let us focus on the instance of the minister of religion. Suppose a pastor, a reputable man, in charge of a parish that provides a very small benefice [*meager financial support*], yet has his eye set on a more prestigious and materially prosperous pastoral opportunity; and suppose his prospects of gaining this advancement are improved if he becomes more studious, if he preaches more frequently and earnestly, and if he adjusts some of his principles to suit the temper of this larger congregation, then for my part I see no reason why a man ought not to pursue this course, provided he receives a call. Yes, and there are other reasons besides these why he should seek this advance in his career, provided he is an honest man. Here are some of them.

1. His desire for a more prosperous parish is lawful, and this beyond contradiction, because it is providence that has set this opportunity before him; so let him pursue it with all of his might without questioning his conscience.[16]

2. Besides, his desire for that parish causes him to be more studious, a more earnest preacher, and so forth, with the result that he becomes a better man. Yes, he is able to improve his person and gifts, and this is certainly according to the mind of *God*.

3. Now as for his complying with the mood of his people, at the expense of his own principles, so as to serve them, this indicates:

---

[16] *A misuse of I Cor. 10:25-27.*

a. He has a self-denying temperament.
b. He has a sweet and winning deportment.
c. He is well qualified for the pastoral office.

4. I conclude then that a pastor who exchanges a small for a larger parish should not be judged as covetous in so doing, but rather, on account of his determination to improve himself, should be esteemed as one who pursues his call, and especially the opportunity at hand, to do good.

And now to the second instance in your question concerning the tradesman you mentioned. Suppose such a person in his business has low profitability, but by becoming religious he may upgrade his opportunities for increased revenue, such as by marrying a rich wife, or something similar, and as a result far more customers come to his shop; for my part I see no reason why this course may not be pursued. And why is this so?

1. It is virtuous to become religious, by whatever means a man may use.

2. It is not unlawful to marry a rich wife, and by this means increase trade profitability.

3. Besides, the man who gets these advantages by becoming religious, obtains that which is good through a good means so that he himself becomes good; as a result a good wife is obtained, and good customers, and good profit, and all of these through becoming religious, which in itself is good. Therefore to become religious to get all of these is a good and profitable pursuit.

This answer offered by *Mr. Money-love* in response to *Mr. By-ends*' question was loudly applauded by them all. Therefore they concluded that the whole answer was most wholesome and worthwhile.[17] And because they were convinced that no one could possibly contradict this argumentation, and because *Christian* and *Hopeful* were still within calling distance, they gladly agreed to challenge them with the question as soon as they were able to overtake them, and especially because of the opposition that *Mr. By-ends* had earlier faced.

So they called ahead to them, and *Christian* and *Hopeful* stopped and waited until the party of four had caught up. But the challengers concluded that rather than *Mr. By-ends*, it would

---

[17] *Prov. 12:23; 13:20; 15:2, 14.*

be preferable for old *Mr. Hold-the-world* to propose the question to the two pilgrims; the reason for this was that any reply to him would be without any remaining heated feelings that had been kindled between *Mr. By-ends* and them at their earlier encounter. So they approached each other and after a short greeting, *Mr. Hold-the-world* proposed the question to *Christian* and his companion. Then he requested that they answer it, that is if they could possibly do so.

CHRISTIAN: Even a babe in religion could answer ten thousand questions of this type. For according to *John 6:26-27*, it is certainly unlawful to follow *Christ* for bread. Then how much more abominable it is to turn he and religion into a stalking horse [*a fake cover and decoy*] for the purpose of obtaining and enjoying the world. The only ones who are of this opinion are the heathen, hypocrites, devils, and witches.

1. The heathen, for when *Hamor* and *Shechem* had a desire for the daughter and cattle of *Jacob*, and they realized that there was no way for these to be obtained except by becoming circumcised, then they addressed their companions: "If every male among us agrees to be circumcised even as they are also circumcised, shall not their cattle and possessions and every beast of theirs become ours?" The daughters and cattle of *Jacob* were that which they plotted to obtain, so that their religious profession became the charade they used to obtain what they coveted. Read the whole story in *Genesis 34:20-23*.

2. The hypocritical *Pharisees* were also of this religion; their long prayers were but a pretense used to convey a pious intent, while in reality they were defrauding widows of their houses. For this reason their judgment from *God* will be greater damnation. Read about it in *Luke 20:46-47*.

3. *Judas* the devil was also of this religion since he worshiped the disciples' money chest and coveted its contents; but he was lost, cast away, and the very son of perdition.[18]

4. *Simon* the witch [*sorcerer*] was of this religion as well, for he coveted the *Holy Spirit* so that by this means he might obtain money; and his sentence from *Peter's* mouth was according to *Acts 8:19-22*.

---

[18] *John 6:70-71; 12:6; 17:12.*

5. Neither does it escape my mind that a man who will take up religion to profit from the world, will also throw away that same religion to suit the world; in the same way *Judas* became religious because of his worldly designs; then he was willing to sell his religion and his *Master* for the same reason. Therefore to answer the question positively as I perceive that you have done is heathenish, hypocritical, and devilish, and your reward will be according to your works.

Then they stood staring at one another without knowing what to say in reply to *Christian*. *Hopeful* fully approved of the soundness of *Christian's* answer, so that there was a great silence amongst them.[19] *Mr. By-ends* and his companions staggered in the face of such a response, and purposely lagged behind so that *Christian* and *Hopeful* might easily get ahead of them. Then *Christian* commented to his fellow pilgrim, "If these men cannot stand before the sentence of mere men, what will they do when confronted with the sentence of *God*? And if they are speechless when dealt with by vessels of clay, what will they do when they are rebuked by the flames of devouring fire?"[20]

Mr. Hold-the World and By-ends

---

[19] *Job 40:3-5; Rom. 3:19; Tit. 1:10-11.*

[20] *Exod. 24:17; Heb. 12:29.*

23
THE SILVER MINE AT THE HILL LUCRE

THEN *Christian* and *Hopeful* moved ahead of *By-ends* and his friends once again. So they traveled until they came to a delicate [*subtle*] plain called *Ease*, across which they journeyed with much satisfaction; though this plain was also narrow so that they quickly passed through it.[1]

Now at the other side of this plain was a small hill[2] called *Lucre* [*Greedy Profit*],[3] and within it a silver mine; and because of the rarity of this place, some pilgrims having gone this way had turned aside to investigate it. However, drawing too near to the edge of the shaft, and because of the treacherous nature of the ground which broke under their feet, they were destroyed.[4] Other pilgrims were known to have been maimed there, and for the rest of their lives were never free from the mine's wounding influence.

Then I saw in my dream that a little off the side of the road, and right next to the silver mine, stood *Demas*. Standing like a gentleman, he would invite passing pilgrims to step aside and investigate the sight; so he hailed *Christian* and his companion. "Hello their friends; come over here and I will show you something quite remarkable."[5]

CHRISTIAN: What could be so deserving of our attention as to draw us out of the way?

DEMAS: Here is a silver mine, and right now some are digging in it for treasure. If you also would come here, with only a little effort you will be able to richly enhance yourselves.[6]

---

1 Pilgrims have very little ease in this life.

2 *Gen. 19:20.*

3 *I Sam. 8:3; I Tim. 3:3, 8; 6:10; Tit. 1:11; I Pet. 5:2.*

4 *Matt. 13:22.*

5 *Col. 4:14; Philem. 24; II Tim. 4:10.*

6 *Prov. 28:20, 22.*

HOPEFUL: If this be true, then let us go and investigate.

CHRISTIAN: Not I! I have previously heard of the reputation of this place and how many have been destroyed here; and besides this, the treasure being promoted is in fact a snare for those who seek it because it hinders them in their pilgrimage.[7]

Then Christian called to *Demas* asking, "Is this not a dangerous place? And has it not hindered many others in their pilgrimage?"[8]

DEMAS: It is not very dangerous, except to those who are careless: (Nevertheless he blushed as he spoke this way.)

CHRISTIAN: (Addressing Hopeful) Let us not wander aside even one step, but instead keep on our way.

HOPEFUL: I give you my word as certain, that when *By-ends* arrives at this place and receives the same invitation as we have, he will definitely turn aside to explore the site.

CHRISTIAN: Undoubtedly he will, for his principles lead in that direction; and I wager a hundred to one that he will perish there.

DEMAS: (Persistently) But will you not come over and look?

CHRISTIAN: (Speaking bluntly) *Demas*, you are an enemy of those who pursue the right paths of the *Lord* of this way. I know that you yourself have been rebuked because of your own turning aside here, and that by one of *His Majesties'* judges;[9] so why do you seek to bring us into the same condemnation? Besides, if we were to turn aside here, our *Lord* the *King* would certainly hear about this and reveal our shame, whereas our desire is to stand before him with boldness.

In reply, *Demas* only pleaded further; he professed to be one of their kinsmen, and proposed that if they would only wait a short while, he would then join them on pilgrimage.

CHRISTIAN: What is your name? Is it not the same as I have already called you?

DEMAS: Yes, my name is *Demas*; I am the son of *Abraham*.[10]

---

7 Hos. 4:16-19; *14:8*; *I Tim. 6:9-10.*

8 *Col. 3:5.*

9 *Acts 13:10*; II Tim. 4:10.

10 *John 8:33, 37-40.*

CHRISTIAN: I know you; *Gehazi* was your great-grandfather, and *Judas* was your father, and you have continued to walk in their ways.[11] What you are now suggesting is simply one of your commonly used devilish tricks. Your father was hanged as a traitor, and you also deserve no better reward. Do be assured that when we have audience with the *King*, we will tell him of your treacherous behavior.

So *Christian* and *Hopeful* continued on their way, though they remained in sight of *By-ends* and his friends; and it was noticed when the trailing party arrived at the silver mine, they immediately left the way in response to the invitation of *Demas*. Now whether they fell down the mine shaft by looking over the edge, or whether they went down to dig, or whether they were smothered at the bottom by the damps [*poisonous fumes of discouragement*] that often arise in those depths, I am not certain. But this I did observe that they were never seen again in the way.

Then *Christian* sang:

> *By-ends*, and *Silver-Demas*, both agree;
> One calls, the other runs, that he may be
> A sharer in his lucre; so these two
> Take up in this world, and no further go.

Demas

---

[11] II Kings 5:20; Matt. 26:14-15; 27:1-6.

24

THE MONUMENT TO LOT'S WIFE

NOW I saw that just on the other side of this plain, the pilgrims came to a place where an old monument stood, right next to the highway. At the sight of this they were both concerned because of the strangeness of its shape, for it seemed to them as if it had been a woman who was transformed into a pillar. Therefore they stood intently looking at it, but for a time they did not know what to conclude.

Eventually *Hopeful* noticed an inscription on the head, though in an unusual style of writing; so being no scholar, he called upon *Christian*, on account of his learning, to see if he could interpret the meaning. So after some study of the letters, he found the meaning to be this, "Remember *Lot's* wife." Then he read it to his companion, and after this they both concluded that it was the pillar of salt into which *Lot's* wife had been turned; this happened when, fleeing from *Sodom* for safety, she looked back with a covetous heart.[1] As a result of this amazing sight, both travelers were stimulated to enter into the following discourse.

CHRISTIAN: Ah my brother, this is a timely sight, for it has come just at the right time after the invitation which *Demas* gave us to step aside from the way and view the *Hill Lucre*.[2] And had we gone over as he desired, and as you were inclined to do, my brother, I suppose it is quite likely that we ourselves would have become a similar spectacle for those who will follow after us.

HOPEFUL: I am sorry that I was so foolish, and the thought of this makes me wonder why I am not now as petrified as *Lot's* wife. For in what way was there a difference between her sin and mine? She only looked back, whereas I had a desire to investigate the mine. Let grace be adored here, and let me be ashamed that such a thought should ever enter my heart.

---

1 Gen. 19:26; *Luke 17:32*.

2 *Jer. 23:14; Rom. 15:4*.

CHRISTIAN: Let us take notice here of what can be profitably learned to help us in the future. This woman escaped one judgment, for she did not suffer the judgment of *Sodom*; however, she was destroyed by another, which, as we see, was her being turned into a pillar of salt.

HOPEFUL: True, and we should allow her to be both a warning and an example. As a warning, we should shun her sin, since her judgment indicates what will befall us if this wayside monument does not restrain us. So *Korah*, *Dathan*, and *Abiram*, with the two hundred and fifty men that perished in their sin, also become a sign or example for others to beware the judgment of *God*.[3]

But above all, I ponder one particular thing, and that is how *Demas* and his friends can so confidently stand over there looking for treasure, while this woman merely looked behind her; for we do not read that she stepped so much as one step out of the way, nevertheless she was turned into a pillar of salt. And the judgment which overtook her remains an example, and within sight of those rummaging in the mine. For if they were to simply lift up their eyes, they could not miss seeing her.

CHRISTIAN: Yes, it is an astonishing thing to contemplate, and it indicates that their heart has grown quite desperate in this case. For I cannot think of what is more fitting for them to be compared with than he who picks pockets in the presence of a judge, or the thief who cuts purses under the shadow of the gallows.

It is said of the men of *Sodom* that "they were exceedingly great sinners" because "they were sinners before the *Lord*," that is within his eyesight, and that notwithstanding the kindnesses that he had showed them, for the land of *Sodom* then was like the *Garden of Eden*.[4] Therefore this provoked him all the more to jealousy, and made their plague as hot as the *Lord* out of *Heaven* could make it. And it is to be reasonably concluded that those, such as we have been talking about, who sin in *God's* sight, yes and in spite of many warnings being continually set

---

3 Num. *16:1-50*; 26:9-10; *I Cor. 10:6, 11.*

4 Gen. 13:10, 13.

before them in calling for repentance, must be judged with the greatest severity.

HOPEFUL: Without doubt, you have spoken the truth. But what a mercy it is that neither you, and especially I, are ourselves not made to be examples as was this woman. Therefore this occasion gives us the opportunity to thank *God*, to fear him, and always to remember *Lot's* wife.

Hopeful

25

CHRISTIAN AND HOPEFUL ARE CAPTURED BY GIANT DEAPAIR

THEN I saw that they went on their way and reached a pleasant river which *King David* called the *River of God*, but *John the Apostle*, the *River of the Water of Life*.[1] Now their way went directly alongside the bank of the *River*. Therefore here *Christian* and *Hopeful* walked with great delight; they also drank of the water of the *River*, which they found to be invigorating to their weary spirits. Furthermore, on either side, the banks of this *River* had green trees that bore every variety of fruit; and the leaves of the trees had good medicinal value.[2]

Now they were particularly delighted with the fruit of these trees, and they also ate the leaves to prevent surfeiting [*gluttony*], and other diseases related to hot bloodedness [*misplaced passion*] in their travels. On either side of the *River* there was also a meadow beautifully adorned with lilies; and it remained green all the year long.[3] So in this meadow they lay down and slept, for here it was a safe place to rest.[4] When they awoke, again they ate of the fruit of the trees and drank of the water of the *River*. Then they lay down to sleep once more. And this they did for several days and nights. Then they sang:

> Behold you, how these Christal [*crystal*] streams do glide
> (To comfort pilgrims) by the highway side;
> The meadows green, besides their fragrant smell,
> Yield dainties for them: and he that can tell
> What pleasant fruit, yes leaves, these trees do yield,
> Will soon sell all, that he may buy this field.[5]

---

[1] Ps. *1:1-3; 46:4*; *65*:9; *Jer. 17:7-8*; Ezek. 47:1-12; *John 4:13-14; 7:37-39*; Rev. 22:1-2.

[2] *Ezek. 47:12; Rev. 22:2.*

[3] *Ps. 23:2, 4-5; Isa. 14:30.*

[4] Ps. 23:2; Isa. 14:30; *Heb. 4:9-10.*

[5] *Matt. 13:44.*

So when they felt it right for them to move forward (for they were not yet at their journey's end), again they ate and drank, and then departed.

Now I beheld in my dream that they had not journeyed very far ahead when the *River* and the way divided and began to go in separate directions. For this reason they were very displeased, though at the same time they were also fearful of leaving the straight path. However as they went on they continued to wish for an easier way. And now that the straight path was heading away from the *River*, it also became more rough and troublesome while at the same time their feet were becoming more tender on account of their travels. So the souls of the pilgrims became increasingly discouraged on account of the harshness of the way.[6]

Now a little ahead of them there was on the left hand side of the road a meadow,[7] and a stile giving access to it over a fence; and that meadow was called *By-Path-Meadow.*[8] Then *Christian* said to his companion, "If this meadow runs alongside of our way, then let us cross over to it." So he went to the stile to investigate, and behold, a pathway on the other side of the fence seemed to run parallel with their way. "This is exactly as I had hoped for," said *Christian*. "Here the going is much easier; so come, my good *Hopeful*, and let us cross over."[9]

HOPEFUL: But what if this new path should lead us out of the way?

CHRISTIAN: That is not likely. Look, does it not run alongside our way, except on the other side of the fence? So *Hopeful,* being persuaded by *Christian*, followed him over the stile.[10]

---

6 Num. *11:4-6*; 21:4-5.

7 *Eccles. 10:2; Matt. 25:33.*

8 At By-Path-Meadow one temptation makes way for another. *Prov. 4:25-27.*

9 *Rom. 14:23.*

10 Strong pilgrims, *even a Peter (Gal. 2:11-14)*, may lead weak ones out of the way.

Now when they had gone over and began to travel along this new path, they found it much easier on their feet. Moreover, on looking ahead of them, they caught sight of a man walking in the same direction as they (and his name was *Vain-confidence*). So they called out to him and asked him where this way led.[11] He then replied, "To the *Celestial Gate*." "Look," said *Christian*, "did I not tell you so? With this advice you can be sure that we are going in the right direction." So they followed and *Vain-confidence* went ahead of them.[12] But behold, the night began to overtake them so that it grew very dark. As a result, they who were behind lost sight of he who was ahead.

Therefore he that was ahead of them, being *Vain-confidence* by name, because he could not see the way ahead of him, fell into a deep pit; it was a trap specially prepared by the prince of that region for the purpose of catching vain-glorious fools so that they might be dashed to pieces in their fall.[13] Now *Christian* and his companion heard him fall. So they called out to learn how *Vain-confidence* was doing; but there was no reply except for some groaning.

Then said *Hopeful*, "Where are we now?" But his friend was silent, for he was now pondering if he had led his brother out of the way.[14] And now it began to rain, with thunder and lightning, in a fearful manner, so that rising water began to flood the path. Then *Hopeful* inwardly groaned while declaring, "If only I had kept in the way I was going!"

CHRISTIAN: Who could have thought that this path would lead us out of the way?

HOPEFUL: From the beginning I was afraid that this would happen, and therefore that is why I gave you a gentle warning. I would have spoken more plainly, but you are older than I [*in the faith*].

---

[11] *Ps. 118:8.*

[12] See what happens to those who quickly listen to the advice of strangers.

[13] *Prov. 14:12*; Isa. 9:16.

[14] *I Cor. 10:12.*

CHRISTIAN: Good brother, do not be offended; I am ever so sorry that I have led you out of the way and exposed you to such impending danger. I earnestly ask you to forgive me; I did not act out of evil intent.

HOPEFUL: Be comforted, my brother, for I forgive you; I also believe that this seeming tragedy shall work out for our good.[15]

CHRISTIAN: I am so glad that I have such a merciful brother traveling with me. But let us not stand here any longer; we must try to return to the right way.

HOPEFUL: In that case, my good brother, let me lead the way.

CHRISTIAN: No, if you please, do let me go first. Then if we encounter any danger I can first deal with it since I am responsible for our getting out of the way.

HOPEFUL: No, you shall not go first because your mind is troubled, and for this reason you may lead us out of the way once again.

Then for their encouragement they heard the voice of one saying, "Let your heart be set toward the highway, even the way that you formerly went along; go back there."[16] But by this time the flood waters had risen much higher and made the way back more dangerous. (Then I understood that it is easier going out of the way, when we are there, than going into the way, when we are out.) Still they made every effort to go back; but it was so dark, and the flood waters had risen so high, that in such an attempt they could have easily been drowned nine or ten times.

Neither were they, with all of their skill and determination, able to return to the stile that night. Therefore, having at last found refuge in a small shelter, they sat down there awaiting daybreak, but being weary, they soon fell asleep.

Now not far from this place where they slept there was a castle called *Doubting-Castle*, the owner of it being *Giant Despair*;[17] and they were lying asleep in his territory. Therefore,

---

[15] *Rom. 8:28.*

[16] Jer. 31:21.

[17] *II Cor. 1:8.*

having arisen early in the morning, while walking up and down in his fields this *Giant* caught *Christian* and *Hopeful* asleep in his realm.

Then with a grim and surly tone to his voice, he ordered then to awaken and tell him where they were from and what they were doing on his property. They replied that they were pilgrims who had lost their way. Then said the *Giant*, "You have trespassed against me by trampling upon and lying on my grounds; therefore, you must come with me." So they were forced to go with the *Giant* because he was stronger than they. And as they went along, they had very little to say because they knew that this circumstance was their own fault. Therefore the *Giant* drove them in front of him, and eventually secured them in his *Castle* by locking then in a very dark dungeon that was so foul and stinking to the spirits of these two prisoners.

Here then they lay, from Wednesday morning until Saturday night, without receiving one bit of bread, a drop of drink, any light whatsoever, or even someone to ask how they were. Therefore they found themselves in an evil situation while being far from friends and acquaintances. So in this place, *Christian's* sorrow was multiplied because it was on account of his hasty advice that they had been brought into this distressing state of affairs.[18]

Now *Giant Despair* had a wife and her name was *Diffidence* [*reticence, mistrust*]; so when he went to bed that evening, he told his wife what he had done, that is how he had taken a couple of prisoners and incarcerated them for trespassing on his grounds. Then he sought her advice as to what he ought to do with them the following day. So she enquired as to who they were, where they had come from, and where they were going; and he told her. Then she advised him that when he arose in the morning, he should beat them without the slightest mercy.

So when he arose, having obtained a fearful crab-tree cudgel [*club*], he went down to the prisoners in their dungeon and began to beat them as if they were dogs, even though they never responded with any disrespect. Then the *Giant* lay into them with his cudgel most fiercely, so beating them that they were

---

[18] Ps. 88:18.

unable to protect themselves or even move on the floor.[19] This done, he left them there to commiserate in their great distress and mourn over their calamity. So for the rest of that day they did nothing else but offer sighs and bitter lamentations.

The next night *Diffidence* talked further with her husband about the prisoners, and on learning that they were still alive, she advised him to recommend to them that they commit suicide. So the next morning he went to the dungeon with a bad-tempered manner as before; on noticing that the prisoners were very sore on account of their previous beating, the *Giant* told them that since they would never be released from their bondage, the only alternative way of escape was for them to commit suicide using either a knife, a noose, or poison.[20] "For why," said he, "should you continue to choose life seeing that it is filled with so much bitterness?"[21]

But the prisoners asked that he let them go, at which the *Giant* scowled as if he was about to rush at them; undoubtedly he would have finished them off then and there, except that he fell into a fit (for sometimes in sunny weather these seizures overtook him whereby he temporarily lost the use of his hands).[22] Therefore he withdrew from the dungeon and left the captives to consider what they ought to do. Then the prisoners discussed amongst themselves whether it would be best for them to take the *Giant's* advice or not. So they entered into intense conversation.

CHRISTIAN: My brother, what shall we do? The life that we now live is miserable. For my part, I do not know whether it is best for us to live as we are, or to die at our own hand. My soul chooses strangling rather than life, and the grave appears more desirable than this dungeon.[23] Shall we accept the *Giant's* advice?

---

[19] On Thursday *Giant Despair* beats his prisoners.

[20] *Job 2:9-10.*

[21] On Friday Giant Despair advises his prisoners to commit suicide.

[22] *John 1:5; 8:12; 12:46.*

[23] Job 7:15.

HOPEFUL: It is a fact that our present condition is dreadful, and death does appear more welcome than this continual misery. But let us consider what the *Lord* of the country to which we are going has to say. He declares, "You shall not commit murder, no not to another man's person." How much more then are we forbidden to take the *Giant's* advice and kill ourselves.[24]

Besides, he who kills another can only commit murder upon his body; but for one to kill himself is to kill both body and soul at the same time. And moreover, my brother, you talk about ease in the grave; but have you forgotten the *Hell* where it is certain that murderers go? For no murderer has eternal life,[25] and much more could be said here.

Also let us again consider that *Giant Despair* does not have authority over all the law of our *Lord*. So far as I can understand, others have been captured by him as well as we, and yet they have escaped out of his hand. Who knows if perhaps the *God* who made this world will cause *Giant Despair* to die? Or that at some time or other he may forget to lock us in? Or that he may shortly have another paralyzing fit right here and lose the use of his limbs? For if ever another seizure happens, for my part I am determined to pluck up manly courage and, with all the effort I can muster, attempt to escape from his hand. I was a fool not to try much earlier; however, my brother, let us be patient and continue to endure;[26] the opportunity may arise that will give us happy relief; but let us not be our own murderers.

And with these words, *Hopeful*, for the present, did calm the mind of his companion; so that day they continued to endure the darkness together, while remaining sad and doleful. Well, towards evening the *Giant* went down to the dungeon once again to see if his prisoners had taken his advice. But when he saw them, they were still alive, though barely so. For on account of the lack of bread and water, as well as the brutal wounds received at their beating, they could now do little more than

---

[24] *Exod. 20:13.*

[25] *I John 3:15.*

[26] *Heb. 6:15; 12:5.*

breathe. But, as I said, he found them alive; at which he fell into a furious rage and told them that, seeing they had disobeyed his counsel, it would now be worse for them than if they had never been born.

At this the prisoners greatly trembled with terror, and I think that *Christian* fell into a swoon; but reviving himself a little, they renewed their conversation about the *Giant's* advice, and whether it might now be best to take it or not. Now *Christian* again seemed more inclined to heed this counsel, but *Hopeful* made his second reply as follows.

HOPEFUL: My brother, remember how valiant you have been up to this point in our journey.[27] *Apollyon* could not crush you, nor, for that matter, could all that you heard and saw and felt in the *Valley of the Shadow of Death*. What hardship, terror, and confusion you have already experienced. So do all of these count for nothing in your present fearful plight? You understand that I am imprisoned with you, a far weaker man by nature than ever you were. Further, this *Giant* has wounded me as well as yourself, and he has deprived me of bread and water even as you; and along with you I detest this darkness. But still let us exercise a little more patience. Remember how you played the man at *Vanity Fair* and were not afraid of the shackles or cage, or even bloody death. Therefore, at least to avoid the shame that a *Christian* ought not to be associated with, let us bear up with patience as well as we can.[28]

Now night having come again, and the *Giant* and his wife being in bed, *Diffidence* asked him concerning the condition of the prisoners and if they had taken his advice. To this he replied, "They are sturdy scoundrels; they would rather choose all manner of hardship than take their own lives." Then she said, "Take them into the *Castle* yard tomorrow and show them the bones and skulls of those you have already dispatched; and promise them that before a week comes to an end, you will tear them in pieces just as you have done with other pilgrims like they."

---

27 *Heb. 10:32.*

28 *I Cor. 10:13: I Pet. 2:20.*

So when the morning had come, the *Giant* went to the prisoners once again and took them into the *Castle* yard where he showed them the remains, just as his wife had directed him. "These," said he, "were once pilgrims as you now are; they also trespassed in my grounds as you have done; so when I thought fit, I tore them in pieces; and so within ten days I will do the same to you.[29] Now go, return to your dungeon once again." And with that he beat them all the way back to their cell. And there they lay all day Saturday in a most miserable condition, just as before.[30]

Now when night had come, and *Mrs. Diffidence* with her husband the *Giant* had gone to bed, they began once again to talk about their prisoners. Moreover, the old *Giant* was amazed that all of his blows and counsel could not bring an end to their lives. To this observation his wife replied, "I fear that they live in hope that someone will come to deliver them, or that they have picklocks [*lock release tools*] hidden on them by means of which they hope to escape." "Yes, and since you say so, my dear," said the *Giant*, "I will search them first thing in the morning."

Well, on Saturday about midnight the prisoners began to pray; and they continued in prayer until almost the break of day.[31] Now a short while before it was daylight, *Christian*, like someone suddenly amazed, broke out with a most passionate exclamation. "What a fool I have been, to lie like this in a stinking dungeon, when I could have just as well walked free. In my chest pocket I have a key called *Promise* that will, I am thoroughly persuaded, open any lock in *Doubting-Castle*." "Then," said *Hopeful*, "that is good news. My good brother, do immediately take it out of your chest pocket and try it."[32]

Then *Christian* took the key from his chest and began to try the lock of the dungeon door; and as he turned the key, the bolt

---

[29] *Rev. 2:10.*

[30] On Saturday Giant Despair threatens that the prisoners will soon be torn in pieces.

[31] *Late Saturday evening through to Sunday morning the pilgrims are moved to pray. Acts 12:5; 16:19-25.*

[32] *Gen. 28:15; Heb. 13:5; Rev. 1:18.*

unlocked and the door flew open with ease, so that *Christian* and *Hopeful* immediately came out.[33] Then he went to the outer door that leads into the *Castle* yard, and with his key this door also opened. After that he went to the [*outer*] iron gate for that needed to be unlocked as well.[34] Now this lock was damnably hard [*devilishly tight*], yet the key did eventually open it. So they thrust open the gate and made their escape with great speed. But as it opened, that particular gate made such a creaking sound that it awakened *Giant Despair* who, hurriedly arising to pursue his prisoners, suddenly felt a paralysis come over his limbs, for his seizures came on him once again so that it was impossible for him to chase after the escapees.[35] Then *Christian* and *Hopeful* went on till they came to the *King's* highway once again, and here they were safe because they were out of the *Giant's* jurisdiction.

Now when they had returned over the stile, they began to consider what could be done at that place to prevent further pilgrims from being deceived by this detour and thus fall into the hands of *Giant Despair*. So they agreed that a pillar should be erected there and plainly engraved with the following warning: "Over this stile is the way to *Doubting-Castle* which is kept by *Giant Despair* who despises the *King* of the *Celestial Country* and seeks to destroy his holy pilgrims." Therefore, many pilgrims that continued to pass by were able to read what was written and so escape this danger.

This being done, *Christian* and *Hopeful* sang as they continued on their way.

> Out of the way we went, and then we found
> What it was to tread upon forbidden ground;
> And let them that come after have a care,
> Lest heedlessness makes them, as we, to fare;
> Lest they, for trespassing, his prisoners are,
> Whose *Castle's Doubting*, and whose name's *Despair*.

---

33 *Acts 16:26.*

34 *Acts 12:10.*

35 *John 1:5.*

26

CHRISTIAN AND HOPEFUL AT THE DELECTABLE MOUNTAINS

THEN they went forward until they came to the *Delectable Mountains*, which belonged to the *Lord* of that *Hill* about which we have spoken before. Thus they drew nearer to the *Mountains* so as to look more closely at the gardens, the orchards, the vineyards, and the fountains of water, where they also drank, and washed themselves, and freely ate of the fruit of the vine. Now on the tops of these *Mountains* there were *Shepherds* feeding their flocks and standing alongside of the highway.[1] Therefore the pilgrims approached them and, as is customary when such travelers are weary and pause to talk, they leant on their staves and enquired, "To whom do these *Delectable Mountains* belong? And who owns the sheep that are feeding here?"

SHEPHERDS: These *Mountains* are *Immanuel's Land* and they are within sight of his *City*; the sheep are also his and he laid down his life for them.[2]

CHRISTIAN: Is this the way to the *Celestial City*?

SHEPHERDS: You are going in the right direction.

CHRISTIAN: How much farther do we have to go?

SHEPHERDS: It is too far for any except those who shall certainly arrive there.

CHRISTIAN: Is the way ahead safe or dangerous?

SHEPHERDS: It is safe for those for whom it is to be safe; but transgressors shall undoubtedly fall along the way.[3]

CHRISTIAN: Is there a place here where pilgrims who are weary and faint may find temporary rest?

SHEPHERDS: The *Lord* of these *Mountains* has given us orders that we should not neglect the provision of hospitality for

---

1 *Luke 2:8.*

2 *Ezek. 34:20-31; Matt. 1:23*; John 10:11, *15*.

3 Hos. 14:9; *John 6:37; II Tim. 2:19.*

strangers.[4] Therefore the refreshing and good features of this place are at your disposal.

I also saw in my dream that when the *Shepherds* recognized that they were wayfaring men [*travelers*], they put some questions to them which were answered as in other places; for instance, "From where have you come?" and, "How did you enter the way?" and, "What means have you used to persevere thus far?"[5] For they understood that few pilgrims who first set out and travel a distance yet show their face at these *Mountains*.[6] But when the *Shepherds* heard their answers and were pleased with them, they looked upon them very lovingly and said, "Welcome to the *Delectable Mountains*."

Now the *Shepherds*, whose names were *Knowledge*, *Experience*, *Watchful*, and *Sincere*, took them by the hand and conducted them to their tents where they partook of a prepared feast. Moreover they said, "We would like you to stay here for a while and become acquainted with us, though even more we recommend that you comfort yourselves with the good health that these *Delectable Mountains* provide."[7] The pilgrims indicated that they would be happy to stay, and so they retired to a restful sleep because it was now very late.

Then I saw in my dream that, in the morning, the *Shepherds* invited *Christian* and *Hopeful* to walk with them upon the *Mountains*. So they joined them and were escorted for a while with a pleasant view on every side. Then the *Shepherds* said to one another, "Shall we show these pilgrims some of the wonders that are to be seen here?" So upon agreeing that they should do this, the guests were first taken to the top of a hill called *Error*, which was very steep on the farthest side; there they were told to look down to the bottom. So *Christian* and *Hopeful* peered down and there at the bottom they saw several men all dashed to pieces having fallen from the top. Then said *Christian*, "What

---

4 Heb. 13:1-2.

5 *I Pet. 3:15.*

6 *Luke 13:23-24.*

7 *Isa. 40:11; Ezek. 34:11-16.*

does this mean?" The *Shepherds* answered, "Have you not heard of those who were led into error through their listening to *Hymenaeus* and *Philetus* with regard to the faith [*doctrine*] of the resurrection of the body?"[8] They answered, "Yes." Then the *Shepherds* replied, "Those who you see lying dashed to pieces at the bottom of this *Mountain* are they; and to this day they have remained unburied, as you can see, being an example to others to take care lest they clamber too high, or come too near the brink of this *Mountain*."

Then I saw that the *Shepherds* took them to the top of another *Mountain* named *Caution*, and directed them to look some distance away. Having done this, the pilgrims thought that they could discern several men walking up and down among a number of tombs.[9] And they noticed that the men were blind because they sometimes stumbled over these tombs, and were unable to find their way out from among them. Then said *Christian*, "What does this mean?"

So the *Shepherds* answered, "Did you not notice, a little below these mountains, a stile that led into a *Meadow* on the left-hand side of this way?" They answered, "Yes." Then said the *Shepherds*, "From that stile there goes a path that leads directly to *Doubting Castle* which is owned by *Giant Despair*. And these men (pointing to those wandering among the tombs) were once on pilgrimage even as you now are, that is until they came to that same stile. And because the right way was rough on their feet in that place, they chose to leave the way and cross over to the *Meadow*, and there they were taken captive by *Giant Despair* and cast into *Doubting Castle*.

Now after they had been kept in a dungeon for a while, the *Giant* eventually put out their eyes and led them to the tombs; there he has left them to wander to this very day, that the saying of the wise man might be fulfilled, "He who wanders out of the way of understanding shall remain in the congregation of the dead."[10] Then *Christian* and *Hopeful* looked at one another

---

[8] II Tim. 2:16-18; *II Pet. 3:17.*

[9] *Mark 5:2-5.*

[10] Prov. 21:16.

while tears streamed down their faces; yet they said nothing to the *Shepherds*![11]

Then I saw in my dream that the *Shepherds* took them to another place located in a valley where there was a door in the side of a hill; so they opened the door and invited the pilgrims to look in. Therefore on looking inside they saw that it was very dark and smoky; they also thought that they heard there a rumbling sound like a fire, as well as the crying of some tormented souls, and in addition they smelt the stench of brimstone.[12] Then *Christian* said, "What does this mean?" The *Shepherds* told them in reply, "This is a *By-way to Hell* where hypocrites are able to enter, that is those like *Esau* who would sell his birthright, or like *Judas* who would sell his *Master*, or like *Alexander* who would blaspheme the gospel, or like *Ananias* and *Sapphira* who would lie and dissemble [*deceive*]."[13]

HOPEFUL: I notice that every one of these, at one time or another, put on a display of going on pilgrimage even as we are now doing. Is that not true?

SHEPHERDS: Yes, and they traveled for quite a great distance as well.

HOPEFUL: Exactly how far was it possible for pilgrims such as these to travel in their day, that is while appreciating the fact that they were miserably cast aside?

SHEPHERDS: Some can go even further, while others cannot reach as far as these *Mountains*.

Then the pilgrims spoke to each other, "We certainly have a need to cry to the *Strong* [*One*] for strength."[14]

SHEPHERDS: Yes, and you will need to use it when it is given to you.

By this time the pilgrims had a desire to press forward, and the *Shepherds* agreed that they should do this. So they all walked together toward the end of the *Mountains*. Then the *Shepherds* said to one another, "Let us show the pilgrims here a view of the

---

[11] *I Cor. 15:10.*

[12] *Gen. 19:24; Luke 16:22-26; Rev. 20:10-15.*

[13] *Gen. 25:29-34; Matt. 26:14-16; Acts 5:1-11; I Tim. 1:20.*

[14] *Eph. 3:14-16.*

gates of the *Celestial City*, provided they have the skill to look through our perspective glass [*telescope*]." So the pilgrims gratefully accepted the invitation; hence they were led to the top of a high hill called *Clear* and given the *Shepherds'* telescope to look through. Then they essayed [*attempted*] to look ahead, but the remembrance of the previous sight that the *Shepherds* had shown them made their hands to shake; with this impediment they could not look steadily through the telescope; yet they thought they saw something like the gate and some of the glory of the place.[15] Then they went on their way and sang:

> Thus by the *Shepherds*, secrets are revealed,
> Which from all other men are kept concealed.
> Come to the *Shepherds* then, if you would see
> Things deep, things hid, and that mysterious be.[16]

When they were about to depart, one of the *Shepherds* gave them a note [*written instructions*] describing the way ahead.[17] Another of them advised the pilgrims to beware of the *Flatterer*.[18] The third told them to take care that they did not sleep on the *Enchanted Ground*.[19] And the fourth commended them to *God's* sustaining mercy as they traveled.[20]

So I [*Bunyan*] awoke from my dream.[21]

---

15 The fruit of slavish fear. *I Cor. 13:12.*

16 *Eph. 4:11-16.*

17 *II Tim. 4:1-2.*

18 *Prov. 29:5.*

19 *Eph. 5:15-16.*

20 *Acts 20:32.*

21 *It may be indicated here that Bunyan was released from the Bedford County Jail for a short period of time, so that what follows is the fruit of further incarceration and renewed "dreaming."*

27

CHRISTIAN AND HOPEFUL FIRST ENCOUNTER IGNORANCE

AND I slept and dreamed again, and saw the same two pilgrims going down the *Mountains* along the highway toward the *Celestial City*. Now a little below these *Mountains* on the left-hand side lies the country of *Conceit*,[1] and from it originates a little crooked lane along which pilgrims walk since it enters into the straight way.[2] Therefore here they met a very brisk lad [*lively young man*] named *Ignorance*. So *Christian* asked him, "From where have you come? And where are you going?"

IGNORANCE: Sir, I was born in the country that lies on our left-hand side, and I am going to the *Celestial City*.

CHRISTIAN: But how do you imagine that you shall gain entrance at the gate? Will you not encounter some difficulty there?

IGNORANCE: Just as other good people have gained entrance there, so will I.

CHRISTIAN: But what acceptable qualification can you show at the gate so that it will be opened for you to enter?

IGNORANCE: I know my *Lord's* will and I have lived a good life; I have repaid every man to whom I was in debt; I frequently pray, fast, pay tithes [*tenths*] and give alms to the poor, and have forsaken the land of my birth so that I might arrive as a pilgrim.[3]

CHRISTIAN: But you did not enter in at the *Wicket-gate*, that is at the commencement of this straight way. Rather you came in here by means of that crooked lane, and therefore I fear, whatever you may think about yourself, that when the day of final reckoning [*judgment*] comes, you will be accused of

---

1 *Prov. 26:12; Rom. 11:25; 12:16.*

2 *Ps. 125:5.*

3 *Isa. 64:6; Luke 18:9-14.*

being a thief and a robber instead of qualifying as a legitimate entrant for the *City*.[4]

IGNORANCE: Gentlemen, you are utter strangers to me; I do not know you, so be content to follow your religion and I will be content to follow mine.[5] I do hope that all will be well. And as for the gate that you talk about, all the world knows that it is a great distance away from our country. I cannot imagine that any man in our regions knows anything about the way to it. Furthermore, there is no need for them to be concerned about it since we have, as you can plainly see, a fine, pleasant, green lane that leads from our country down into the way right here.

When *Christian* understood that this man was wise in his own conceit, he whispered to *Hopeful*, "There is more hope for a fool than him."[6] He further added, "When he who is a fool walks along the way, wisdom is lacking in him, and so he demonstrates to everyone that he is a fool.[7] So shall we talk any more with him? Or shall we walk ahead of him for the present and give him time to think about what he has already heard? And then shall we wait for him further on and see if a gradual approach can more effectually benefit him?" Then *Hopeful* responded:

> Let *Ignorance* a little while now muse
> On what is said, and let him not refuse
> Good counsel to embrace, lest he remains
> Still ignorant of what's the chiefest gain.
> *God* says, Those that no understanding have,
> (Although he made them) them he will not save.

HOPEFUL: I do not think that it is wise to tell him everything at once. Rather, if you agree, let us leave him for a while and then talk to him later, that is when he is better prepared to receive it.[8]

---

4 *John 10:1; 14:6.*

5 Ignorance makes it clear to everyone that he is a fool.

6 Prov. 26:5, 12; *Matt. 6:23; John 9:39-41.*

7 Eccles. 10:3.

8 How to deal with a fool. *Prov. 14:7.*

28

THE TERRIFYING END OF TURN-AWAY

SO the two pilgrims went on while *Ignorance* followed after them. Now when they had put some distance ahead of him, they entered into a very dark lane where they met a man who seven devils had bound with seven strong cords;[1] they were carrying him back to the door that they had earlier seen in the side of the *Hill*, when being escorted by the *Shepherds*.[2]

Now good *Christian* began to tremble and so did his companion *Hopeful*. Yet as the devils led the man away, *Christian* looked to see if he could identify him, and he thought it might be a certain *Turn-away* who resided in the *Town of Apostasy* [*Departure from the Faith*]. But he was not able to clearly see his face because he hung his head down like a thief who has been discovered. However, after he had passed by, *Hopeful* watched as he was taken away and noticed on his back a label with the inscription, "Wanton [*licentious*] professor [*believer*], and damnable [*Hell consigned*] apostate."[3]

Turn-away captive to seven devils

---

1 Prov. 5:22; Matt. 12:45; *Eph. 4:17-18.*

2 *Jude 4, 13.*

3 *I John 2:18-19.*

29

THE COLORLESS TESTIMONY OF LITTLE-FAITH

THEN *Christian* said to his companion, "Now it comes to my mind what was told to me about something that happened to a good man in this region. The name of this man was *Little-faith*, as I said a good man, and he lived in the *Town of Sincere*.[1] What happened to him was this; there is an entrance to the straight way here that comes down from *Broad-way-gate*[2] by means of a lane called *Dead-man's Lane*; this lane is so-called because of the murders that are frequently committed there."

"And so this *Little-faith*, while going on pilgrimage just as we are, happened to sit down for a while and then fell asleep. It also happened at that time that three sturdy rogues came down the lane from *Broad-way-gate*; and their names were *Faint-heart*, *Mistrust*, and *Guilt* (three brothers), and when they saw where *Little-faith* was snoozing beside the way, they immediately made a quick approach toward him. Now the good man was just awakening from his slumber and preparing to continue on his journey. So they all approached him with threatening language and ordered him to stand still. At this *Little-faith* turned as white as a sheet since he had neither the strength to fight nor to flee. Then *Faint-heart* said, 'Hand over your purse.'"

"But when *Little-faith* hesitated to comply, for he was very reluctant to lose his money, *Mistrust* came close to him and, thrusting his hand into one of his pockets, pulled out of there a bag of silver. Then he [*Little Faith*] cried out, 'Thieves! Thieves!' At this *Guilt* struck *Little-faith* on his head with a large club in his hand, so that the blow felled him flat on the ground; and there he lay, bleeding profusely in danger of dying."

"During this assault, the thieves simply stood by. But eventually they heard the sound of another coming along the way, and fearing that it could be *Great-grace* who lives in the city of

---

1 *Matt. 6:30; 8:26; 14:31; 16:8; Eph. 6:24; Phil. 1:10.*

2 *Mat. 7:13.*

Good-confidence, they quickly departed and left the poor victim to fend for himself. Now after a while, *Little-faith* began to revive; so he scrambled to his feet and staggered along as best he could. This was the story."

HOPEFUL: But did the robbers take from him everything that he had?

CHRISTIAN: No, they never ransacked his chest pocket where his jewels were; he was able to keep these.[3] But I was told that this good man was sorely troubled over what he lost. For the thieves took most of his spending money. As I have already mentioned, they did not get his jewels; other than these he was left with a small amount of money, but hardly enough to support him through to his journey's end.[4] Sad to say, if I have not been misinformed, he was forced to beg along the way in order to have enough to stay alive, for he was not able to sell his jewels. So he continued to beg and scrape around; yes, he went forward, but often with an empty stomach for most of the remaining journey.

HOPEFUL: But is it not remarkable that they did not rob him of his certificate, that which he must have to gain entrance into the *Celestial City*?

CHRISTIAN: Yes, it is a wonder; but they did not get it. Though they did not miss it on account of the cunning of *Little-faith*, for since he was so dismayed by their onslaught, he had neither the strength nor the skill to hide anything. So it was more a question of good providence rather than his ingenuity that caused them to miss such a vital item.[5]

HOPEFUL: Nevertheless, it must have been a comfort to him that they did not take away his jewels.

CHRISTIAN: It could have been a great comfort to him if he had rightly appreciated this fact.[6] But they that related this story to me explained that he made little reference to this matter for the rest of his journey, the reason being his dismay that they had

---

[3] Little-faith did not lose his best things.

[4] I Pet. 4:18.

[5] II Tim. 1:14; *II Pet. 2:9.*

[6] II Pet. 1:19.

taken his money away. Yes, he forgot about his jewels for a great part of the remainder of his journey; and besides, when at times his mind was comforted with the contemplation of his jewels, yet thoughts about his monetary loss would rise up again and overwhelm his previous comfort.

HOPEFUL: How sad for this man! Such a situation must have been the cause of great grief to him.

CHRISTIAN: Yes, he was deeply distressed, and would we not have been like him if we had similarly been robbed and wounded in a strange place such as he was? It is surprising that he did not die with grief, poor soul! I was told that, for the remainder of his journey, he chiefly spread abroad melancholy and bitter complaints concerning his misfortune. He would also explain in detail to other pilgrims encountered in the way where and how he was robbed, who they were who assaulted him, what he lost, the severity of his wounds, and the closeness of his brush with death.[7]

HOPEFUL: But what a wonder it is that the demands of traveling did not compel him to sell or pawn some of his jewels so that pressures along the way might be relieved.

CHRISTIAN: You talk with about as much wisdom as that of a newborn chicken with some shell still stuck on its head![8] Why would he ever want to pawn his jewels? And to whom would he sell them? In that region where he was robbed his jewels were not even considered valuable, nor did he desire the sort of relief that the citizens there might offer. Besides, had his jewels been discovered as missing at the gate of the *Celestial City*, he well knew that he would certainly be excluded from receiving an inheritance there; and for him, such a consequence would have been regarded as worse than meeting with the belligerence of ten thousand thieves.

HOPEFUL: My brother, why are you so sharp with me? *Esau* sold his birthright for a mere mess of pottage; and surely that

---

7 *Rom. 15:1; I Thess. 5:14.*

8 Christian snibbeth [*rebukes*] his companion for his thoughtless comment.

birthright was his most precious jewel.[9] So if he sold such a treasure, then why could not *Little-faith* do the same?

CHRISTIAN: It is true that *Esau* did sell his birthright, and besides this so have many others; and by so doing they have excluded themselves from the chief blessing, as indeed that caitiff [*indulgent coward*] did. But you should recognize a fundamental difference between *Esau* and *Little-faith*, and also between their spiritual conditions. *Esau's* birthright was typical, but *Little-faith's* jewels were not so. *Esau's* god was his belly, but Little-faith's belly was not so. *Esau's* lack lay in his fleshly appetite,[10] but this was not true of Little-faith. Besides, *Esau* could see no further than the fulfilling of his lusts. He said, "For I am at the point of death, so what good will this birthright do me?" But *Little-faith*, though it was appointed for him to have only a little faith, yet by means of his little faith he was kept from many extremes.[11] So by means of this same faith he was enabled to prize his jewels rather than sell them, as *Esau* did with his birthright. You will not read anywhere that *Esau* had faith, no not so much as a little.

Therefore it is not surprising in the case of Esau, when the flesh alone controls a man, and it undoubtedly does when faith that works resistance is absent; for he will then readily sell his birthright and his soul and everything, even to the *Devil* in his *Hell*. Such a person may be likened to the ass who in her periods of heat, cannot be made to change direction.[12] When their minds are fastened upon their lusts, they will have them whatever the cost. But *Little-faith* was of a different disposition; his mind was focused on things divine; his livelihood was based upon spiritual things that originate from *Heaven*.[13]

Therefore, for what purpose would a person of this temperament sell his jewels, supposing that someone might have bought them, so as to fill his mind with empty things? Will a man give a

---

[9] Heb. 12:16-17.

[10] Gen. 25:30-34.

[11] *Heb. 11:6.*

[12] Jer. 2:24.

[13] Little-faith could not live on Esau's pottage.

penny to fill his belly with hay? Or can you persuade the turtle-dove to live upon carrion [*carcass meat*] like the crow? Though faithless ones will pawn, or mortgage, or sell what they have, and even themselves outright as well, all for the sake of carnal lusts, yet they that have faith, true saving faith, though but a little of it, cannot do so. Therefore my brother, here is your mistake.

HOPEFUL: I frankly acknowledge it. But at the same time, your severe response has almost made me angry.

CHRISTIAN: Yes, I was rather harsh, but I did it to compare you with certain birds that are especially lively, and run to and fro in untrodden paths with the shell on their heads, like a newborn chick! But let us leave this matter behind and consider the matter under discussion, and all will be well between you and me.

HOPEFUL: But *Christian*, I am persuaded in my heart that these three fellows were nothing more than a company of cowards. Otherwise, do you think that they would have been so quick to run at the sound of someone else approaching along the way? So why did not *Little-faith* pluck up greater courage? It is my opinion that he could have resisted at least one skirmish with them, and then yielded when they overwhelmed him.[14]

CHRISTIAN: Certainly many have called these assailants cowards, but in reality few have found this to be true during an actual period of trial. As for *Little-faith* having a great [*courageous*] heart, he had no such thing.[15] And I believe that had you been the man concerned, after a short engagement you would have quickly yielded. To be truthful, while you are churned up about this matter when these opponents are distant from us, I believe you might have second thoughts about a brave confrontation if they should reappear to challenge you.[16]

---

[14] Hopeful swaggers [*is very opinionated*].

[15] There is no great heart for God where there is little faith.

[16] We have more courage when we are distant from spiritual assaults than when we are close.

But consider again that these travelers are in fact hired thieves who serve under the *King* of the bottomless pit;[17] he himself, when needed, will quickly come to their aid, and his voice is like the roaring of a lion.[18] I myself have been engaged in a conflict like that of *Little-faith*, and I found it to be a terrifying experience. These three villains also set upon me, and while I began to resist them as a *Christian* ought, yet they were quick to call for their master's assistance, which was immediately forthcoming. As the saying goes, I would have exchanged my life for a mere penny, but, as *God* would have it, I was clothed [*accoutered*] with armor of proof [*tried armor*]. Even so, though I was well equipped, I found it hard work to prove myself as a manly pilgrim. No one can possibly understand what it is like to experience such combat, except he who has been in the thick of the battle himself.

HOPEFUL: Well, of course, these rogues did retreat when they anticipated that *Great-grace* was possibly drawing close in the way.[19]

CHRISTIAN: True, they were accustomed to fleeing, and even their master, when there was the prospect of *Great-grace* appearing; however, this is not surprising since he is renowned as the *King's* champion. But I trust you will make some distinction between *Little-faith* and the *King's* champion.[20] All the *King's* subjects are not his champions; nor can they, when tested by assailants, accomplish such valiant feats of war as he does. Is it reasonable to expect that a little child should confront *Goliath* as *David* did? Is it right to expect a wren [*small bird*] to have the strength of an ox? Some pilgrims are strong while others are weak; some have great faith, and others have little. This man *Little-faith* was one of the weaker kind, and therefore he went to the wall [*suffered exhausting humiliation*].

HOPEFUL: I still wish that *Great-grace* had appeared for the sake of those scoundrels.

---

[17] *Rev. 9:1-2, 11.*

[18] I Pet. 5:8.

[19] *Acts 4:33.*

[20] *I Sam. 17:4.*

CHRISTIAN: If he had arrived on that occasion, he might have had his hands full. For I have to tell you that although *Great-grace* is highly skilled with his weapons, as long as he maintains a sharp sword he can do very well against such opponents:[21] yet if *Faint-heart*, *Mistrust*, or *Guilt*, can penetrate his armor, he will find the going hard and even take a fall. And as you know, when a pilgrim is down, what can he do?

Whoever looks very closely at the face of *Great-grace* will notice scars and cuts there that will clearly prove what I say to be true. Concerning one engagement that he had with the enemy, I heard it reported that he had exclaimed about this battle, "We despaired even of life."[22] Is it not true that these sturdy rogues and their accomplices were able to make even *David* groan and mourn and roar with anguish?[23] Yes, and also *Heman*[24] and *Hezekiah*[25], even though regarded in their day as champions, nevertheless they as well were forced to arouse themselves because of the severity of the assaults they faced. And in spite of taking a fearless stand, yet their soiled and torn coats indicated subjection to brutal handling. On one occasion *Peter* tried to do what he could in a similar confrontation; but though he has been acknowledged by some as the prince of the apostles, still these assailants so roughed him up that at the end he was afraid of a pitiful girl.[26]

Besides, the *King* of these scoundrels is always at their beck and call; when they whistle, he is always within their hearing. So if at any time they are losing in battle, whenever possible, he comes to their rescue.[27] And for this reason it has been said of him, "The sword that attempts to strike him cannot succeed, nor can the spear, the dart, or the javelin. He regards iron as straw,

---

[21] *Eph. 6:17.*

[22] *II Cor. 1:8-10.*

[23] *Ps. 38:1-10.*

[24] *Ps. 88:1-18.*

[25] *Isa. 36:1-38:22.*

[26] *Luke 22:31, 54-62.*

[27] *Ps. 7:2; I Pet.5:8.*

and bronze as rotten wood. The arrow cannot make him flee. Sling stones are turned by him into stubble. Darts are regarded as straw. He laughs at the rattling of the javelin."[28] Hence in this case, what can a pilgrim do?

It is true that if a man has full access to *Job's* horse, and has the courage and skill to ride him, then he might accomplish notable deeds for his *King*. It has also been said about this stallion, "For his neck is clothed with thunder; he will not be afraid like the jumping locust; the snorting of his nostrils is terrifying; he paws in the valley while rejoicing in his strength, and then goes forth to engage the armed enemy. He mocks at fear and is frightened of nothing; he would never turn his back from a confronting sword. The quiver trembles at him, as do the flashing spear and javelin. He races over the ground as if devouring it, on account of his fierceness and rage; neither does the trumpet sound cause him to halt. Rather, at the sound of the trumpet he exclaims, 'Aha,' and is drawn by the smell of distant battle, the thundering of captains and the shoutings of conflict."[29]

But for such mere footmen [*infantry*] as you and I are, let us never eagerly desire to meet with an enemy, nor promote ourselves as if we could do so much better, that is when we hear about others who have suffered defeat or a bludgeoning; nor let us be tickled [*proudly stimulated*] with thoughts about our own spiritual manliness, for those who think this way usually suffer the worst when tried.[30] Take *Peter* for example, concerning whom I earlier spoke about. How he would swagger [*strut*]; yes, he really would. Because of his vain attitude, he would promote himself as being more ready to stand in defense of his *Master* than all other men. But tell me, who was more foiled [*defeated*] and exhausted than he when these villains were on the attack?[31]

Therefore when we hear that such robberies take place on the *King's* highway, there are two things that we should do.

---

[28] Job 41:26-29. Leviathan's sturdiness.

[29] Job 39:19-25.

[30] *Rom. 12:3; I Cor. 10:12.*

[31] *Matt. 26:33, 75.*

First, let us be well harnessed [*accoutered with weapons*], and especially sure that we have a shield with us. For it was the lack of this item that made it impossible for the vigorous assailant of *Leviathan* [*the ferocious monster*] to make him yield.[32] For it is certainly true that if this particular weapon is missing, then he [*the King of the bottomless pit*] will have no fear of us. That is why one of the *King's* champions [*Paul*] has advised, "Above all take the shield of faith with which you will be able to extinguish the fiery darts of the wicked one."[33]

Second, as we travel, it is good for us to request the *King* that he provide shepherding guides, and that he go with us himself. This prospect made *David* rejoice when he was passing through the *Valley of the Shadow of Death*. Also *Moses* expressed his preference for death rather than tread one more step without *God*.[34] Oh my dear brother, if our *King* alone will go with us, why should we be afraid even though thousands shall plot to oppose us; but on the other hand, without him the proud can only find refuge under the corpses of the wicked who have been slain.[35]

For my part, I have been in the thick of the battle before now, and though I am presently alive through the goodness of he who is best, yet I cannot boast in my spiritual manliness. I shall be ever so glad if I do not meet with any further clashes, though I fear we have not passed beyond all danger. However, since the lion and the bear have not yet devoured me, I have hope that *God* will deliver us from the next uncircumcised *Philistine*.[36] Then *Christian* sang:

> Poor *Little-faith* has been among the thieves!
> Was robbed! Remember this, whoever so believes
> And gets more faith, shall then a victor be[37]
> Over ten thousand, else scarce over three.

---

[32] *Job 41:1-34.*

[33] Eph. 6:16.

[34] Exod. 33:13-15; Ps. 3:5-8; *23:4.*

[35] Ps. 27:1-3; Isa. 10:4.

[36] *I Sam. 17:26-36; Prov. 28:15; Jer. 47:4.*

[37] *I John 5:4.*

30

CHRISTIAN AND HOPEFUL SNARED BY THE FLATTERER

SO they went on and *Ignorance* followed behind. They continued until they came to a place where another path joined in with the straight way. Now this new alternative way seemed as straight as the road to which they had become accustomed. Because of this the pilgrims were undecided as to which way they should take, for each seemed as straight as the other. So they stood still and pondered.[1]

And as they were wondering which way to take, a black man, dressed in a light colored robe, approached them;[2] he then asked the pilgrims why they were standing there. They explained that they were going to the *Celestial City*, but did not know which of the two ways to now take. "Follow me," said the man, "for it is the way in which I am now going." So they followed him along the new way that had joined the old way, though this new path gradually veered away from the *Celestial City* so that they came to be facing the opposite direction. Now as time passed by, before they awakened to their guide's deception, he led both pilgrims into a net that completely closed itself around them. As a result they became so thoroughly entangled that they did not know what to do. Then the white robe fell off the black man's back so that the captives began to understand what had happened. Therefore they lay crying for some time because they did not know how to escape.

CHRISTIAN: Now I understand that I have been caught in an error. Did not the *Shepherds* exhort us to beware of the flatterers? Today we have found to be true that which the wise man has declared, "A man that flatters his neighbor also spreads a net for his feet."[3]

---

1 *Prov. 14:12.*

2 *Prov. 4:19; Eph. 5:11.*

3 Prov. 29:5.

HOPEFUL: They also gave us written instructions showing directions along the way so as to ensure our safe arrival; but we have forgotten to study them, and so have not kept ourselves from the paths of the destroyer. At this point *David* was much wiser than we for he said, "Concerning the deeds of men, by the word of your lips I have kept from the paths of the destroyer."[4] So they continued to bemoan themselves while lying enmeshed in the net.

At last they noticed a *Shining One* coming toward them with a small whip made of thin cord in his hand.[5] When he had drawn near to the place where they were ensnared, he asked them from where they had come. They told him that they were poor pilgrims going to *Mount Zion*, but had been led out of their way by a black man clothed in white. "He advised us," they said, "to follow him since he professed to be going to *Mount Zion* as well." Then the *Shining One* with the whip responded, "This person was the *Flatterer*, a false apostle, who has transformed himself into an angel of light."[6] So he tore open the net and let the men out.

Then he ordered them, "Follow me so that I may redirect you back to the way again." So he led them back to the old straight way which they had left to follow the *Flatterer*. Then he asked them, "Where did you stay last night?" They replied, "With the *Shepherds* on the *Delectable Mountains*." Then he asked them. "Did they give you written instructions that included a map for the way ahead?" They replied, "Yes." But the *Shining One* pressed further, "When you came to a halt here, did you refer to the map for guidance?" They answered, "No." So he asked them, "Why?" They replied, "We forgot." Then he asked, "Did the *Shepherds* exhort you to beware of the *Flatterer*?" They answered, "Yes, but we did not imagine that this fine-spoken man could possibly be he."[7]

Then I saw in my dream that the *Shining One* commanded the pilgrims to lie down; having done this, he severely chastised

---

4 Ps. 17:4.

5 *John 2:15.*

6 Dan. 11:32; II Cor. 11:13-14.

7 Rom. 16:17-18.

them so as to teach them the good way in which they should walk; and while he was whipping them he declared, "As many as I love, these I also rebuke and discipline; therefore be zealous and repent."[8]

Having done this, he directed them to be on their way and pay particular attention to the other directions of the *Shepherds*.[9] So thanking him for all of his kindness, they very softly proceeded along the right way,[10] while singing:

> Come hither, you that walk along the way;
> See how the pilgrims fare, that go astray!
> They are caught in an entangling net,
> 'Cause they good counsel lightly did forget;
> 'Tis true, they rescued were, but yet you see,
> They're scourged as well; let this your caution be.

The Flatterer

---

[8] Deut. 25:1-2; II Chron. 6:26-27; *Heb. 12:5-11*; Rev. 3:19.

[9] *Prov. 12:28.*

[10] *I Kings: 21:27; Isa. 38:15.*

31

CHRISTIAN AND HOPEFUL MEET RETURNING ATHEIST

NOW after a while, they noticed someone in the distance coming softly and alone along the highway to meet them. Then said *Christian* to his companion, "Ahead of us is a man with his back toward *Mount Zion*, and he is coming to meet us."

HOPEFUL: I see him, so let us be very careful now lest he should prove to be another flatterer.

So this man drew nearer and nearer until he came right up to them. His name was *Atheist*, and he immediately asked the pilgrims where they were going.

CHRISTIAN: We are going to *Mount Zion*.

ATHEIST: (Having burst into howling and scornful laughter) I cannot but help laugh on account of it being so obvious that you are both ignorant persons; for you have committed yourselves to a very tiring journey that will provide you with absolutely nothing for your trouble, other than a fruitless journey.

CHRISTIAN: Why man, do you think it possible that we will not be received at our destination?

ATHEIST: Received! But there is no such place that you dream of in all this world.[1]

CHRISTIAN: But there is in the world to come.[2]

ATHEIST: When I was at home in my country of origin, I also heard about what you are saying; and it was for this reason that I set out in search of this *Celestial City*, over twenty years ago. But from the day that I departed until now, no such place has ever been discovered.[3]

---

[1] *Ps. 14:1; Prov. 18:2.*

[2] *John 18:36; Heb. 13:14.*

[3] Eccles. 10:15; Jer. *17:15*; 22:13.

CHRISTIAN: Both of us have heard about such a place and we definitely believe that it is possible to find it.

ATHEIST: Had I not first believed as you do, I would not have come this far in my search. You would think that I ought to have found such a place by now. But having traveled further than you have, I am returning home where I hope to refresh myself with the things that were earlier cast aside for a vain hope.[4]

CHRISTIAN: (Seriously addressing *Hopeful*) Is it true what this man is telling us?[5]

HOPEFUL: Be very careful, for this fellow is definitely one of the flatterers. Remember what it has already cost us for our listening to another sweet-talker like this one. What a thing to say, that there is no *Mount Zion*! Did we not see the very gate of the *City* from the top of the *Delectable Mountains*? Furthermore, are we not to walk by faith rather than sight?[6] So let us be on our way lest the man with the whip should catch up with us again.

But my good companion, you should have been the one teaching this lesson to me. So let me plainly address you in both ears: "My son, cease listening to instruction that will cause you to depart from the words of knowledge."[7] I tell you my brother, do not listen to this man any more, but rather let us believe unto the saving of the soul.[8]

CHRISTIAN: My brother, let me confess that I did not put that question to you on account of my own personal doubt of the truth. Rather, my intention was to test you and draw forth a response that indicated the real commitment of your heart. And as for this man, I know well that he is blinded by the god of this world.[9] So let you and I go forward knowing that we have right

---

4 Atheist desires worldly contentment. *II Pet. 2:22.*

5 Christian tests his brother.

6 Hopeful's gracious answer. II Cor. 5:7.

7 Prov. 19:27.

8 Heb. 10:39.

9 *II Cor. 4:4; Rev. 12:9.*

belief of the truth, for no lie or false testimony can be of the truth.[10]

HOPEFUL: Now I do rejoice in hope of the glory of *God*.[11]

So both pilgrims turned away from *Atheist* while he, raucously laughing, went on his way.[12]

Temporary

[10] I John 2:21.

[11] *Rom. 5:2; I John 3:2.*

[12] *Rom. 1:18-25.*

32

CHRISTIAN AND HOPEFUL CROSS THE ENCHANTED GROUND

THEN I saw in my dream that the travelers continued on their way until they came to a particular region where the nature of the air had a tendency to make one drowsy, that is with regard to strangers passing through. And it was here that *Hopeful* began to feel lethargic and sleepy. Therefore he spoke to *Christian*, "I have now become so drowsy that I can hardly keep my eyes open; so let us lie down here and take a nap."[1]

CHRISTIAN: In no way, my brother, lest in sleeping we never awaken again.[2]

HOPEFUL: Friend, why do you say that? To the working man sleep is very sweet;[3] in taking a nap we will be refreshed and feel much better.

CHRISTIAN: Do you not remember that it was one of the *Shepherds* who exhorted us to beware of the *Enchanted Ground*? By this he meant that we should be careful not to doze there. So let us not sleep as others do, but rather let us watch and be sober.[4]

HOPEFUL: I do confess myself at fault, and had I been traveling here alone, by sleeping I would have been in danger of death. How true is the saying of the wise man, "Two are better than one."[5] Up to this point in our journey, your companionship has been a continual mercy; be assured that you shall have a good reward for your efforts.

CHRISTIAN: Now then, to prevent drowsiness in this place, let us commence with some profitable conversation.

HOPEFUL: Why, I wholeheartedly agree.

---

1 *Prov. 6:9-10.*

2 *Ps. 13:3.*

3 *Eccles. 5:12.*

4 I Thess. 5:6.

5 Eccles. 4:9.

CHRISTIAN: Then where shall we begin?

HOPEFUL: Well, let us start where *God* began to work with us. But if you are agreeable, do begin first.

When saints do sleepy grow, let them come hither,
And hear how these two pilgrims talk together;
Yes, let them learn of them in any wise [*way*]
Thus to keep open their drowsy slumbering eyes.
Saints' fellowship, if it be managed well,
Keeps them awake, and that in spite of *Hell*.[6]

A. Hopeful Testifies to His Conversion at Vanity Fair

CHRISTIAN: (Suggesting a topic to *Hopeful*) Let me ask you a question. How did you first come to think about what you are doing now?

HOPEFUL: Do you mean, how did I first come to be concerned about the healthy condition of my soul?

CHRISTIAN: Yes, that is exactly what I mean.

HOPEFUL: For a long time I continued to delight in those things which were on display and marketed at *Vanity Fair*; these were things which I now believe, had I continued in them, would have certainly led to my eternal damnation and destruction.[7]

CHRISTIAN: What were these things in particular?

HOPEFUL: All of the treasures and riches of the world. Also, I derived great pleasure from rioting, partying, drinking, swearing, dishonesty, lewdness, Sabbath-breaking, and much more, all of which tended to destroy my soul.[8] But at last I discovered that, by listening to and thinking about spiritual truth, this ungodly lifestyle would eventually lead to my death; I further understood that because of these carnal things the wrath of *God* falls on the children of disobedience.[9] Such truths I

---

6 The Dreamer's note.

7 *I Tim. 6:9.*

8 Hopeful's life before conversion. *This is similar to Bunyan's early lifestyle described in Grace Abounding, §§ 4, 8, 22, 26. Gal. 5:19-21.*

9 Rom. 6:21-23; Eph. 5:6.

heard from you, as well as beloved *Faithful* who was put to death for his faith and godly living in *Vanity Fair*.

CHRISTIAN: And did this new understanding bring about an immediate burden of conviction?

HOPEFUL: No, because right then I was not willing to know about the evil of sin or the damnation that results from obeying it; on the contrary, when troubled with the *Word* of truth, I made every effort to shut my eyes to its revealing light.

CHRISTIAN: But what was the cause of your continual resistance to these first workings of *God's* blessed *Spirit* upon you?

HOPEFUL: The causes were:

1. I was ignorant that this was the work of *God* upon me. I never understood that by means of awakening me to sin in my life, *God* first begins the conversion of a sinner.

2. Sin was very sweet to my flesh and I was most reluctant to forsake it.

3. I could not contemplate parting with my established worldly companions, for their friendship and lifestyle continued to be desirable to me.

4. Those periods in which convictions seized me were so troublesome and fearful to my heart that I could not endure them, no not so much as the mere remembrance of them.

CHRISTIAN: Then it would seem that sometimes you were able to be rid of your trouble.

HOPEFUL: Yes, that is true, but then it would return again into my mind so that I would be as bad, no even worse than I was before.

CHRISTIAN: Tell me then, what was it that brought your sins to mind again?

HOPEFUL: Many things, such as:

1. If I merely met a good man in the street; or,
2. If I heard anyone read from the Bible; or,
3 If my head began to ache; or,
4. If I was told that some of my neighbors were sick; or,
5. If I heard the bell toll for someone who had died; or,
6. If I thought of my own dying; or,
7. If I heard that others had suddenly died; or,
8. But especially, when I considered my own imminent appointment with judgment.

CHRISTIAN: And at any time could you easily be relieved of this guilt of sin, that is when any of these incidents confronted you?

HOPEFUL: No, not more recently, for on appearing they seemed so rapidly to grasp hold of my conscience. And then, if I did contemplate returning to my sin, though my mind was in opposition to this, the result would be double torment for me.

CHRISTIAN: And what did you think of doing then?

HOPEFUL: I concluded that I must make every effort to improve my life, otherwise I believed I was certain to be damned.

CHRISTIAN: And did you actually carry out this resolve to reform your life?

HOPEFUL: Yes, and I fled from not only my sins, but also sinful company as well. Furthermore, I devoted myself to religious duties such as praying, Bible reading, weeping over my sin, speaking the truth to my neighbors, and other matters. I was involved with so many of these practices that they are too numerous to mention.

CHRISTIAN: And did you regard yourself as better off on account of this religious involvement?

HOPEFUL: Yes, that is for a while; but eventually greater trouble seemed to overwhelm me and rise way above the level of my reformations.

CHRISTIAN: How could that possibly come about since you confessed to attaining reformation [*improvement*] in your life?

HOPEFUL: There were several thing that brought this upon me, and especially sayings such as these, "All our righteousnesses are as filthy rags," and "By the works of the law no man shall be justified," and "When you have done all things, say, We are unprofitable," and many more like these besides.[10] So from this I began to reason with myself as follows; if all my righteousnesses are as filthy rags, and if no man can be justified by the deeds of the law, and if when we have done all, we are still unprofitable, then it is sheer folly to think of attaining *Heaven* be means of the law. I further thought as follows: if a man runs up a debt of a hundred pounds at a local shop, and then

---

[10] Isa. 64:6; Luke 17:10; Gal. 2:16.

subsequently pays cash for everything else that he buys, still the original debt will remain unsettled; and in this case the shopkeeper will probably sue him and have the debtor imprisoned until he pays the debt in full.[11]

CHRISTIAN: Yes I understand, but how does this apply to yourself?

HOPEFUL. Well I reasoned as follows concerning my own condition. Because my sins cause me to be greatly indebted in *God's* book, and all of my present reforming will not pay for what I owe, therefore I should ponder what use are all of these new improvements. For how shall I escape from the damnation that endangers me on account of my former transgressions?

CHRISTIAN: That is a very good application. But I do ask that you continue.

HOPEFUL: Another thing that troubled me, even concerning my recent amendments, was this; if I looked very closely into the best of what I now do, I still see sin, new sin, mixing itself with the best of what I do.[12] So now I was forced to conclude that, notwithstanding my former fond conceits regarding myself and my duties, yet I had committed enough sin in one duty to send me to *Hell*, even though my former life had been faultless.

CHRISTIAN: And what did you then do?

HOPEFUL: What did I do? Why I was at a loss to know which way to turn, that is until I laid bare my heart to *Faithful*; for he and I were well acquainted with each other. So he told me that unless I could obtain the righteousness of a man who had never sinned, then neither mine own nor all of the righteousness of the world could save me.[13]

CHRISTIAN: And were you convinced that he spoke the truth?

HOPEFUL: Had he told me this when I was pleased with my own improvements, then I would have called him a fool for his trouble; but now, having seen my own corruption, and the sin that is attached to my own best performances, I have been forced to agree with his opinion.

---

11 *Gal. 3:10.*

12 *Rom. 7:21.*

13 *Job 25:4-6.*

CHRISTIAN: But when he first recommended to you a man who could rightly be described as being sinless, did you believe that such a person could be found?

HOPEFUL: I must confess that at first this recommendation sounded strange, but after some further discussion and fellowship with *Faithful*, I became fully convinced that he was right.

CHRISTIAN: And did you ask him to identify this man and explain how you might be justified by him?[14]

HOPEFUL: Yes, and he told me it was the *Lord Jesus Christ* who dwells at the right hand of the *Most High*. So he explained, "You must be justified by him, that is by trusting in what he accomplished in the days of his flesh when he suffered by hanging on the tree [*cross*]."[15] Then I further asked, "How is it that this man's righteousness could be effectual in justifying another man before *God*." And he told me that he was the mighty *God*,[16] and that what he did in dying was not for himself, but for me. Furthermore, the righteousness of his doings [*obedient atoning work*] and their worthiness [*acceptability*] would be imputed [*reckoned*] to me if I believed on him.

CHRISTIAN: And then what did you do?

HOPEFUL: I offered objections as to why I should not believe, and especially because I thought this *Christ* was not willing to save me.

CHRISTIAN: And what did Faithful then say?

HOPEFUL: He urged me to go to him and find out for myself. But I replied that I thought this was presumptuous. However, he said that this was not so since I was invited to come.[17] Then he gave me a book of *Jesus* in which were his very words, and these only all the more encouraged me to freely come to him. He added that every jot and tittle in this book were more firmly established than *Heaven* and *Earth*.[18] So I

---

[14] Rom. 4:1-5.

[15] Col. 1:21-22; Heb. *5:7-9*; *7:26*; 10:11-22; I Pet. 1:3-9; *2:24*.

[16] *Isa. 9:6.*

[17] Matt. 11:28-30; *John 7:37.*

[18] Matt. *5:18*; 24:35.

asked him what I must do when I came to *Christ*; he told me that I must first fall to my knees and plead with all of my heart and soul that the *Father* would reveal him to me.[19]

Then I asked him how I should make my entreaty to this *Jesus*. He responded that I should go and find him sitting on a mercy-seat where he sits throughout each year providing mercy and forgiveness for those who come to him.[20] Then I told him that I would not know what to say when I did come. And he directed me to speak in this manner, "*God*, be merciful to me a sinner, and enable me to know and believe in *Jesus Christ*;[21] for I understand that if his righteousness was not available, or I did not have faith in that righteousness, then I would be utterly rejected. *Lord*, I have heard that you are a merciful *God* and have ordained that your *Son Jesus Christ* should be the *Savior* of the world;[22] and moreover, I understand that you are willing to confer him [*and his salvation*] upon poor sinners such as myself, and indeed I am a poor sinner. Therefore *Lord*, take this opportunity to magnify your grace in the salvation of my soul, through your *Son Jesus Christ*. Amen."

CHRISTIAN: And did you do exactly as you were told?

HOPEFUL: Yes, over and over and over again.

CHRISTIAN: And did the *Father* reveal his *Son* to you?

HOPEFUL: Not on the first, the second, the third, the fourth, the fifth, or even the sixth occasion.

CHRISTIAN: Then what did you do?

HOPEFUL: What did I do? Why I could not tell what to do.

CHRISTIAN: Did you ever consider giving up on praying?

HOPEFUL: Yes, at least a hundred times, and then another hundred.

CHRISTIAN: And why was it that you did not give up?

HOPEFUL: I believed that what had been told me was true, that is that without the righteousness of this *Christ*, all of the world could not save me. And therefore I thought to myself, if I

---

19 Ps. 95:6; Jer. 29:12-13; Dan. 6:10.

20 Exod. 25:22; Lev. 16:9; Num. 7:8-9; Heb. 4:16.

21 *Luke 18:13.*

22 *John 1:29; 4:42; I John 4:14.*

cease making these entreaties, then I die; though I can only die at the throne of grace. And moreover, this came to my mind, "If it delays, then wait for it, because it will certainly come, and will not delay."[23] So I continued praying until the *Father* revealed his *Son* to me.[24]

CHRISTIAN: And how was he eventually revealed to you?

HOPEFUL: I did not see him with my physical eyes, but rather with the eyes of my understanding.[25] Now this is how it happened. One day I was particularly sad;[26] I think I was more sad [*spiritually depressed*] than at any other time in my life; and this bout of sadness came about through a fresh sight of the greatness and vileness of my sins. So as I was then anticipating nothing else but *Hell* and the everlasting damnation of my soul, suddenly, I thought I saw the *Lord Jesus* look down from *Heaven* toward me and beckon me with this invitation, "Believe on the *Lord Jesus Christ*, and you shall be saved."[27]

But I replied, "*Lord*, I am a great, indeed a very great sinner;" to this he answered, "My grace is sufficient for you."[28] Then I said, "But *Lord*, what exactly is it to believe?" Immediately I understood from that saying, "He who comes to me shall never hunger, and he who believes on me shall never thirst,"[29] that believing and coming mean the same thing. Therefore, he who comes to *Christ*, that is runs to him because of a heart overflowing with earnest desires for salvation by *Christ*, is he who truly believes in *Christ*. I further heard him say, "And he

---

[23] Hab. 2:3.

[24] *Matt. 11:27.*

[25] Eph. 1:18-19.

[26] *Hopeful's conversion here parallels that of Bunyan in Grace Abounding where he also describes "one day" when conviction of personal sin seemed to overwhelm him, § 115.*

[27] Acts 16:30-31.

[28] II Cor. 12:9. *This was Bunyan's cry in Grace Abounding, §§ 204, 206.*

[29] John 6:35.

who comes to me, I will in no way cast out."[30] Then I said, "But *Lord*, how must I properly think about you in coming to you; that is, how should my faith rightly behold you?" Then he responded, "*Jesus Christ* came into the world to save sinners. He is the end of the law for righteousness to everyone who believes. He died for our sins, and rose again for our justification. He loved us, and washed us from our sins in his own blood. He is the mediator between God and us. He ever lives to make intercession for us."[31]

From all of this I came to understand that I must look for righteousness in his person, and for satisfaction for my sins through his blood; and that what he did in obedience to his *Father's* law, and in submitting to its attending penalty, was not for himself, but for he who will accept it for his salvation and be thankful. As a consequence, my heart now became full of joy while my eyes flooded with tears; now my affections overflowed with love for the name, people, and ways of *Jesus Christ*.

CHRISTIAN: This was truly a revelation of *Christ* to your soul. But tell me in more detail what effect this encounter had upon your spirit?

HOPEFUL: It made me understand that all of the world, notwithstanding its vaunted righteousness, is yet in a state of condemnation. It made me see that *God the Father*, while being just, can also justify the coming [*believing*] sinner.[32] It made me greatly ashamed of the vileness of my former lifestyle and amazed that I could be so ignorant in this condition. For up till that time no thought had come to my heart that revealed the beauty of *Jesus Christ*.[33] It made me love a holy life and long to do something for the honor and glory of the name of the *Lord Jesus*. Yes, I now considered that if I had a thousand gallons of blood in my body, I would gladly spill it all for the sake of the *Lord Jesus*.

---

30 John 6:37.

31 Rom. 4:25; 10:4; I Tim. 1:15; *2:5*; Heb. 7:24-25.

32 *Rom. 3:26.*

33 *Isa. 33:17.*

B. Closer Reacquaintance is Made with Ignorance

I then saw in my dream that *Hopeful* looked back and saw *Ignorance*, who they had earlier left behind, following after them. "Look," said he, to Christian, "how far that youngster is lagging behind us."

CHRISTIAN: Yes, yes, I see him, though he does not care for our companionship.

HOPEFUL: But I am sure that it would not have hurt him if he had decided to walk with us up to this point.

CHRISTIAN: That is true, though I am certain that he thinks very differently.

HOPEFUL: Yes, I agree with you here; however, let us wait for him to catch up (which they did).

Then *Christian* spoke to *Ignorance*, "Man, come and walk with us. Why do you lag behind us?"

IGNORANCE: Because I find it pleasurable to walk alone, and much more so than with company, that is unless I find some likeable travelers.

Then *Christian* said to *Hopeful* (though softly), "Did I not tell you that he has no desire for our company? However, do join me in conversation with him so that we can better pass the time of day in this solitary place." Then *Christian* addressed *Ignorance* with some questions, "My friend, how are you keeping at the present? How is your relationship between *God* and your soul?"

IGNORANCE: Well, I have hope that it is good right now; as I walk along, I always seem to be full of good motions [*notions*] that come to mind and comfort me.

CHRISTIAN: What are some of these good notions? Do tell us.

IGNORANCE: Why, I think about *God* and *Heaven*.

CHRISTIAN: So do the devils, and souls that are consigned to *Hell*.[34]

IGNORANCE: But I think about them and desire them.

---

[34] *Jas. 2:19.*

CHRISTIAN: So do many who are never likely to reside there. The soul of the sluggard desires *Heaven* and yet has no inheritance there.[35]

IGNORANCE: But I think about them and leave all that I have to obtain them.

CHRISTIAN: I doubt that very much, for to leave everything that you have is much harder to do than many are aware of. But why, or by what evidence are you persuaded that you have left all for *God* and *Heaven*?

IGNORANCE: My heart tells me so.

CHRISTIAN: The wise man declares, "He who trusts his own heart is a fool."[36]

IGNORANCE: But that saying refers to an evil heart, whereas mine is a good one.[37]

CHRISTIAN: But how can you prove that your heart is as good as you say?

IGNORANCE: Because it comforts and assures me concerning my hope of reaching *Heaven*.

CHRISTIAN: That may well be, though on account of its deceitfulness; for a man's heart may minister comfort with regard to his hope of something, even though he has no grounds for expecting the fulfillment of that hope.

IGNORANCE: But my heart and life are in agreement [*harmony*] with one another, and therefore my hope is well grounded.

CHRISTIAN: Who told you that your heart and life are in good harmony?

IGNORANCE: My own heart tells my this.

CHRISTIAN: My dear fellow, ask yourself if I am a thief. So your heart tells you so! Except the *Word of God* bears witness in this matter, any other testimony is of no value.

IGNORANCE: But is it not a good heart that produces good thoughts? And is it not a good life that is in harmony with *God's* commandments?

---

35 *Prov. 13:4.*

36 Prov. 28:26.

37 *Luke 18:11; Rom. 7:24.*

CHRISTIAN: Yes, it is a good heart that produces good thoughts, and it is a good life that is in harmony with *God's* commandments. But it is one thing to really have these qualities, and quite another to only think so.

IGNORANCE: Then tell me, what count as good thoughts and a good life according to *God's* commandments

CHRISTIAN: There are good thoughts of various kinds, some with regard to ourselves, some *God*, some *Christ*, and some other things.

IGNORANCE: What are good thoughts with regard to ourselves?

CHRISTIAN: Those that are in agreement with the *Word of God*.

IGNORANCE: When do thoughts about ourselves agree with the *Word of God*?

CHRISTIAN: When we pass the same judgment upon ourselves which the *Word of God* does. But let me explain further. The *Word of God* says of the natural man, "There is no one who is righteous; there is no one who does good."[38] It also says, "That every imagination of the heart of man is only evil, and continually so."[39] And again, "The imagination of man's heart is evil from his youth."[40] Now then, when we think of ourselves in this sense, then our thoughts are good ones because they are in agreement with the *Word of God*.

IGNORANCE: But I will never believe that my heart is that bad.

CHRISTIAN: If that be so, then you have never had one good thought about yourself in your whole life. But let me continue. As the *Word of God* passes judgment upon our heart, so it also passes judgment upon our ways [*actions*]; and when the thoughts of our hearts, as well as our actions, are in agreement with the judgment that the *Word* brings upon both, then both types of thoughts are good because they are in agreement with that *Word*.

IGNORANCE: Please explain your meaning here.

---

[38] Rom. 3:10-12.

[39] Gen. 6:5.

[40] *Gen. 8:21.*

CHRISTIAN: Why, the *Word of God* says that man's ways are crooked ways; they are perverse, not good. It says that by nature they veer from the good way and have no inclination to know it.[41] Now when a man seriously considers his ways in this manner, I mean when he is sensitive and full of heart-humiliation in his thinking, then he has good thoughts about his own ways because his thoughts now agree with the judgment of the *Word of God*.

IGNORANCE: Then what exactly are good thoughts about *God*?

CHRISTIAN: They are similar to what I have said concerning ourselves. In other words they are good thoughts about *God* when they agree with what the *Word of God* says about him. And so we should think about his character and attributes exactly as the *Word* teaches us, though I cannot presently speak about this in more detail.

However, to speak about *God* concerning ourselves, that is when we understand that he knows us better than we know ourselves, that he can see sin in us when we cannot see it ourselves, then we have right thoughts about *God*. When we understand that he knows our innermost thoughts, and that our heart, to its very depths, is always open to his scrutiny; also, when we know that all of our righteousness stinks in his nostrils, and that even with our best performances we still cannot stand with acceptable confidence before him, then we know that we have right thoughts about *God*.

IGNORANCE: Do you think that I am such a fool as to regard *God* as not being able to see any further than I do? Do you believe that I hope to come to *God* for acceptance offering only the best of my performances

CHRISTIAN: Then tell me, what do you believe about this matter?

IGNORANCE: Why, to come to the point, I consider that I must believe in *Jesus Christ* for justification [*right standing with God*].

CHRISTIAN: But how could you consider believing in *Jesus Christ* when you do not see any need of him? You see neither

---

41 Ps. 125:5; Prov. 2:15; Rom. 3:17.

your original sin nor your actual transgressions; rather you have such an opinion of yourself and what you do that you plainly qualify as one who has never acknowledged the necessity of *Christ's* personal righteousness to justify you before *God*. How then can you possibly say, "I believe in *Jesus Christ*"?

IGNORANCE: In spite of what you say, I believe well enough.

CHRISTIAN: Exactly what is it that you believe?

IGNORANCE: I believe that *Jesus Christ* died for sinners, and that I shall be justified before *God* from the curse [*of the law*] through his gracious acceptance of my obedience to his law.[42] Or to put it another way, *Christ* makes my religious duties acceptable to his *Father* by virtue of his merits, and for this reason I shall be justified.[43]

CHRISTIAN: Let me give an answer to this confession of your faith.

1. You believe with a fantastical [*imaginary*] faith, for such a faith is nowhere described in the *Word of God*.

2. You believe with a false faith, because it takes away the personal righteousness of *Christ* from justification and replaces it with your own.

3. This faith makes *Christ* a justifier of your actions rather than you as a person; then your person is justified for the sake of your actions, and this is patently false.

4. Therefore this faith of yours is deceitful, and of the type that will leave you subject to the wrath of *God Almighty* at his day of final judgment. For true justifying faith directs the soul, being sensitive of its lostness through the law, to flee for refuge to *Christ's* righteousness.[44] Now this righteousness of *Christ* is not an act of grace by which he makes your obedience a justifying work that is acceptable to *God*; rather it is his personal obedience to the law in doing and suffering for us that which

---

42 *Rom. 4:5; Gal. 2:16.*

43 *There is a strong distinction made at this point between grace infused via personal merit and church sacraments, and free grace or justifying righteousness imputed through faith alone in Christ's objective, perfect, once-for-all atonement.*

44 *Num. 35:11-12; Heb. 6:18.*

this same law justly required of us. Let me stress that true faith accepts this righteousness of *Christ* as if it were a skirt by which the soul may be completely covered;[45] so by this means the soul is presented as spotless before *God*, and he accepts it and acquits such a covered person from condemnation.

IGNORANCE: What are you saying? Would you have us trust in what *Christ* in his own person has done without [*outside of*][46] us? This conceit would certainly encourage the loosening of the reigns that restrict our lusts, and allow us to live as we are inclined. For what does it matter how we live when we may be justified from all our sin by *Christ's* personal righteousness, that is when all that we have to do is simply believe?[47]

CHRISTIAN: You are fittingly named *Ignorance*, for you are also ignorant as a person; your answer clearly demonstrates this to be true. You are ignorant of what justifying righteousness is, and equally as ignorant as to how the soul may be safe from the severe wrath of *God* through faith in it. Yes, you are also ignorant of the true [*resultant*] effects of saving faith in this righteousness of *Christ*; these include the conquest and winning over of the heart to *God* in *Christ*, so that it loves his name, his *Word*, his ways, and his people, and not as you ignorantly imagine.

HOPEFUL: Ask him if he has ever had *Christ* revealed to him from *Heaven*.[48]

IGNORANCE: What now is this? Are you a man influenced by revelations? I believe that what you, and all the rest of your persuasion, say about this matter is nothing more than the fruit of distracted brains [*an addled mind*].[49]

HOPEFUL: Why man, *Jesus Christ* is so hid in *God* from the natural understanding of all flesh that he cannot be savingly known by any man, that is unless *God* the *Father* reveals him to them.

---

45 *Gal. 3:26-27.*

46 *This archaic meaning describes Christ's objective righteousness.*

47 *Rom. 6:1, 15.*

48 *Matt. 16:16-17; Gal. 1:15-16.*

49 Ignorance angles [*baits*] them.

IGNORANCE: That is your faith, but it is certainly not mine. On the other hand, I have no doubt that my faith is as good as yours; though in no way do I have as many fanciful notions in my head as you do.[50]

CHRISTIAN: Do allow me to add a further word here. You should not speak so scornfully of this matter; for I will boldly assert, even as my good companion has done, that no one can know *Jesus Christ* except through the revelation of the *Father*.[51] Yes, and I will add as well that even the faith that lays hold upon *Christ*, that is assuming that it is true faith, must be wrought [*forged*] by the exceeding greatness of his mighty power.[52] Now concerning this faith, I observe, poor *Ignorance*, that you are wholly ignorant of it. Therefore, wake up and acknowledge your own wretchedness, and then fly to the *Lord Jesus*; for only by his righteousness, which is the righteousness of *God*, he himself being *God*, shall you be delivered from condemnation.

IGNORANCE: You go so fast that I cannot keep up with you; so do go on ahead as before, and I will follow on some distance behind.

Then the pilgrims said:

> Well *Ignorance*, will you yet foolish be,
> To slight good counsel, ten times given thee?
> And if you yet refuse it, you shall know
> Before long the evil of your doing so.
> Remember man in time; stoop, do not fear,
> Good counsel taken well, saves, therefore hear;
> But if you yet shall slight it, you will be
> The loser, *Ignorance*, I'll warrant thee.

Then *Christian* addressed his companion.

CHRISTIAN: Well, come with me my good friend *Hopeful*, for I see that you and I must walk by ourselves once again.

So I saw in my dream that they went on ahead at a steady pace while *Ignorance* limped along behind. Then *Christian* said to his companion, "I feel great pity for this man, because in the end his journey will come to a woeful conclusion."

---

[50] Ignorance speaks critically about that which he is ignorant.

[51] Matt. 11:25-27; I Cor. 12:3; Eph. 1:18-19.

[52] *Eph. 1:19.*

HOPEFUL: Sad to say, in our *Town* there is an abundance of his kind, whole families, yes even whole streets with many being pilgrims as well. So if there are many like him in our locality, then there must be a great multitude in the place where he was born.

CHRISTIAN: This is true for the *Word* says, "He has blinded their eyes lest they should see," etc.[53] But now that we are by ourselves, tell me what you think of such men. Do you think that at any time they have convictions of sin, and as a consequence have fears about the danger of their condition?

HOPEFUL: No, I would rather that you answer this question yourself since, being older, you have more experience.

CHRISTIAN: Then I would say, at least it is my opinion, that at times they may have such fears. But because they are naturally ignorant of spiritual truth, they do not understand that these convictions contribute toward their good; and therefore they strive with great effort to stifle them while presumptuously flattering themselves concerning the way [*good state*] of their own hearts.

HOPEFUL: I do agree with what you say, for fear does tend to benefit men such as when, at the beginning of their pilgrimage, they are prompted to go the right way.

CHRISTIAN: Without a doubt this is what happens, that is it is right fear. For in this regard the *Word* says, "The fear of the *Lord* is the beginning of wisdom."[54]

HOPEFUL: How would you describe right fear?

CHRISTIAN: True or right fear is identified in three ways.

1. By its arousal. It is caused by saving convictions of sin.
2. It drives the soul to seize hold of [*believe in*] *Christ* for salvation.
3. It gives birth to and maintains in the soul a great reverence for *God*, his *Word*, and ways; so this same soul is kept tender by making it afraid to turn from these affections, either to the right hand or to the left, or to anything that may dishonor *God*, rend its peace, grieve the *Spirit*, or cause the enemy to speak [*of God*] reproachfully.

---

[53] *Isa. 6:9-10; John 12:39-41.*

[54] Job 28:28; Ps. 111:10; Prov. 1:7; 9:10.

HOPEFUL: Well spoken my brother, for I believe that you have said the truth. Have we now almost passed through the *Enchanted Ground*?

CHRISTIAN: Why do you ask? Have you become weary of this present conversation?

HOPEFUL: Not at all, but I would still like to know where we are.

CHRISTIAN: We now have no more than two miles to go in this region. Nevertheless, let us return to the topic under discussion. Now in general, the ignorant do not appreciate that such convictions of sin tend to cause them to fear, and thus are for their good; therefore they seek to stifle them.

HOPEFUL: Be more specific. How do they seek to stifle them?

CHRISTIAN: There are four ways.

1. They think that those fears are forged by the devil, though in fact they are the work of *God*, and in thinking this way they resist them as things that would cause their overthrow [*defeat*].

2. They also think that these fears tend to spoil their faith, even though as deluded poor men they do not have any, and therefore they harden their hearts against them.

3. They presume that they ought not to have fears, and therefore in spite of them, they put on a vain show of confidence.

4. They appreciate that these fears tend to strip them of their pathetic displays of self-righteousness; therefore they resist them with all of their might.

HOPEFUL: I confess to knowing something of this in my own experience; for before I knew the truth about myself, my condition was just as pitiful.

C. Christian Recalls his Acquaintance with Temporary

CHRISTIAN: Well, let us now leave our neighbor *Ignorance* by himself and decide upon another topic that is profitable for discussion.

HOPEFUL: I agree with all my heart; but still, you begin with a suggestion.

CHRISTIAN: Well then, about ten years ago, did you ever know a person named *Temporary* who came from your part of the country? At that time he was very enthusiastic about religion.

HOPEFUL: Did I know him? Yes I certainly did, for he resided in *Graceless*, a town about two miles away from *Honesty*, and he lived next door to one named *Turn-back*.

CHRISTIAN: That is right, for *Turn-back* and he lived in the same terrace of houses. Well, at one time that man was very much awakened; I believe that he then had some appreciation of his sinfulness, and of the wages that were due to him in this regard.

HOPEFUL: I am of the same opinion as you, since, my house being less than three miles from him, he would frequently come to me while his face streamed with tears. I truly pitied that man, and I was not altogether without hope for him; but as one comes to understand, it is not everyone who cries out "*Lord*, *Lord*" [*who proves to be a genuine pilgrim*].[55]

CHRISTIAN: He once told me that he was determined to go on pilgrimage, just as we presently are; but all of a sudden he became a friend of one *Save-self*, and after that he became a stranger to me.[56]

HOPEFUL: Now since we are talking about him, let us enquire a little more closely into the reasons for his sudden backsliding and others like him.

CHRISTIAN: This may be very profitable, but you be the one to begin.

HOPEFUL: Well then, in my judgment there are four reasons for this falling away.

1. Though the consciences of such men are awakened, yet their minds are not changed. Therefore, when the power of guilt fades away, that which stimulated them to become religious ceases to have any effect. Therefore they naturally turn to their former walk once again. We see this same reaction with a dog who becomes sick on account of what he has eaten; in continuing to be sick, he also continues to vomit; he does this

---

[55] *Matt. 7:21-22.*

[56] *Matt. 13:5-6, 20-21.*

not because of a free mind, if it can be said that a dog has a mind, but rather because his stomach troubles him. But when his sickness is ended, so his stomach is troubled no more, and he is no longer opposed to his vomit. So he turns about and licks it all up. And so it is true which is written, "The dog returns to his own vomit again."[57] Now I say that a person may be hot and enthusiastic for *Heaven*, chiefly because of a sense of fear regarding the torments of *Hell*; but as their sense of *Hell's* terror, with its attending fears of damnation, diminishes, so also do their desires for *Heaven* and salvation cool as well. So then it comes to pass that when their guilt and fear are gone, likewise their desires for *Heaven* and happiness die, and they return to their former course once again.

2. Another reason is this; they have slavish fears that overwhelm them. Now I speak here of fears that they have of men, "for the fear of men brings a snare."[58] So then, though they seem to be hot for *Heaven* while the flames of *Hell* are about their ears, yet when that terror abates a little, they propose to themselves some second thoughts; one is that it is good to be wise and not run the risk of losing all for something they know little about; another is that it is not prudent to bring themselves into unavoidable and unnecessary troubles; so they choose to fall in with the world once again.

3. The shame that attends religion also lies as a roadblock in their way; they are proud and haughty, and in their opinion religion is low and contemptible. Therefore when they have lost their sense of *Hell* and the wrath to come, they again return to their former ways.

4. Pangs of guilt and the thought of terror are extremely distressing to them; they prefer not to see their misery before they come to it. Though it is possible that the first sight of it, that is if they appreciate such a view, might make them flee to that refuge where the righteous hide and are safe. Yet because they do, as I hinted before, shun any thinking about guilt and terror, therefore, when they are eventually rid of those stirrings

---

[57] II Pet. 2:22.

[58] Prov. 29:25.

about the terrors and wrath of *God*, they gladly harden their hearts and choose ways that will harden them all the more.

CHRISTIAN: You are pretty close to the heart of this matter, for at the root of this problem in such people is a lack of any change in the mind and will. And therefore they are like the criminal who stands trembling and quaking before the judge; he appears to repent most heartily; but at the bottom of all this is his hatred of the noose, and not any detestation of his crime. This becomes evident when such a man is set free, for then he will continue to be a thief and a rogue. However, if his mind had been changed, he would live differently.

HOPEFUL: Now that I have explained the reasons for his backsliding, do point out to me the manner of his falling away?

CHRISTIAN: I will do so most willingly.

1. They draw away as much of their thinking as they can from the remembrance of *God*, death, and judgment to come.

2. Then they gradually neglect their private duties such as private prayer, the reigning in of their lusts, watchfulness, sorrow for sin, and the like.

3. Then they shun the company of lively and warm Christians.

4. After that, they grow cold toward public duty such as careful listening, reading of the *Word*, godly corporate worship, and the like.

5. Then they begin to pick holes [*find fault*], as we say, in the coats [*lives*] of some of the godly; their devilish intent is to charge that religion is stained, on account of some weaknesses they have detected in these believers, and thus justify putting religion behind their backs.

6. Then they begin to attach themselves to and associate with men who are carnal, immoral, and depraved.

7. Then they yield to carnal and depraved conversation in secret; and they are glad if they can discover similar practices in those who are reputed to be honest, for these hypocrites only encourage them to be all the more bold.

8. After this they begin to play with little sins more openly.

9. And then, having become hardened, they reveal themselves for what they are. Therefore, in being launched again into the gulf of misery, unless a miracle of sovereign grace prevents it, they perish everlastingly in the ocean of their own deceit.

33
THE COMFORTING DELIGHTS OF BEULAH LAND

NOW I saw in my dream that by this time the pilgrims, having traversed the *Enchanted Ground*, then entered into the country of *Beulah* [*Married*].[1] With the way passing directly through it, the air in that place was found to be very sweet and pleasant, so they rested and took comfort there for a time. Yes, here they continually heard the singing of birds, while every day they enjoyed the blooming of various flowers in the land, and also listened to the voice of the turtle-dove. In this country the sun shines day and night.

Therefore it is beyond the influence of the *Valley of the Shadow of Death*, as well as the reach of *Giant Despair*. In fact from this vantage point, *Doubting Castle* was quite out of view. Here the pilgrims were in sight of the *Celestial City* to which they were going;[2] here also they were able to meet some of the inhabitants[3] of that place. For in this land some of the *Shining Ones* walked quite frequently, because it was located upon the very borders of *Heaven*. In this land also the contract between the bride and the bridegroom was renewed. Yes here, "As the bridegroom rejoices over the bride, so did their *God* rejoice over them."[4]

Here they had no lack of corn and wine,[5] for in this place they began to reap in abundance what they had been seeking for throughout their pilgrimage.[6] Here they heard voices wafting across from the *City*, loud voices proclaiming, "Say to the

---

1 S. of S. 2:10-12; Isa. 62:4.

2 *Ps. 107:28-30.*

3 Angels.

4 Isa. 62:4-12.

5 *Frequent biblical expression for material and spiritual blessing. Gen. 27:28, 37; Deut. 33:28; Ps. 4:7; Zech. 9:17.*

6 Isa. 62:8-9.

daughter of *Zion*, Behold your salvation comes, behold his reward is with him." Here all of the inhabitants of the country called them "the holy people, the redeemed of the *Lord*, sought out," etc.[7]

Now as they walked in this land they experienced more rejoicing than in other parts that were more remote from the kingdom to which they were headed. But now drawing nearer to the *City*, they had a much more perfect view of it. It was built of pearls and precious stones, while the streets were paved with gold.[8] As a result of the natural glory of this *City*, and the reflection of the sunbeams upon it, *Christian* became sick with longing;[9] *Hopeful* also suffered periodic bouts of the same disease. Therefore they lay for a while in front of this vista, and continued to cry out, because of recurring pangs, "If you see my beloved, tell him that I am sick by reason of love."[10]

Yet being strengthened a little, and thus more able to endure their sickness, they walked along the way and came nearer and nearer to the *City*. On either side were orchards, vineyards, and gardens with their adjacent entrances being open to enable easy access from the highway.

Now having come closer to these places, the pilgrims noticed the *Gardener* standing in the way; so they asked him, "To whom do these good vineyards and gardens belong?" He answered, "They are the *King's*, and have been planted here for his own pleasure as well as the comfort of pilgrims."[11] So the *Gardener* led them into the vineyards and invited them to refresh themselves with the surrounding delicacies. He also pointed out the *King's* walks and shady nooks which he so enjoyed. So there *Christian* and *Hopeful* paused and slept for a while.

Now I noticed in my dream that they talked more in their sleep at this time than they had ever done in all of their

---

[7] Isa. 62:11-12.

[8] *Rev. 21:18-21.*

[9] *Prov. 13:12.*

[10] *S. of S. 2:5; 5:8.*

[11] Deut. 23:24.

journey.[12] So as I was deeply pondering the reason for this, the *Gardener* spoke even to me [*Bunyan*]: "Why are you deep in thought about this matter? It is the nature of the fruit and grapes of these vineyards to be so sweet and digestible as to cause pilgrims such as these to talk and chatter in their sleep."[13]

The Gardener

---

[12] *I Pet. 1:8.*

[13] *S. of S. 7:9.*

34

CHRISTIAN AND HOPEFUL ENCOUNTER THE RIVER OF DEATH

SO I saw that when they awoke, they prepared themselves to go up to the *City*. But, as I said before, the reflections of the sun upon the *City* were so extremely glorious, for the *City* was pure gold, that they could not behold it with an open face, at least not yet; rather they had to view it through an instrument specially made for that purpose.[1] So I saw that as they moved forward, two men met them who were dressed in clothing that shone like gold; their faces also shone radiantly like light.

These men asked the pilgrims from where they had come, so they told them. They also asked them where they had lodged, what difficulties and dangers they had met with, as well as what comforts and pleasures they had experienced along the way; so they told them. Then these *Shining Ones* advised the pilgrims that they had only two more difficulties to deal with before they gained entrance into the *City*.[2]

Then *Christian* and his companion asked these men to accompany them along the remainder of the way ahead, and the *Shining Ones* agreed to this. But they also explained that the two pilgrims must complete the journey through their own faith. So I saw in my dream that they went on together until they came within sight of the gate of the *City*.

Now I further saw that between them and the gate was a *River*, but there was no bridge so that pilgrims might cross over; moreover, the *River* was very deep. So *Christian* and *Hopeful* were shocked at such a sight; but the men escorting them declared, "You must pass through this *River* or else you cannot arrive at the gate of the *City*. Then the pilgrims asked if there was any other way to the gate.[3] The *Shining Ones* answered,

---

1 *Ex. 30:29-35*; II Cor. 3:18; Rev. 21:18.

2 *Crossing the River of Death and entrance at the Celestial City.*

3 Death is not welcome to nature though by it we pass out of this world into glory.

"Yes, but no one else has been permitted to travel that way since the foundation of the world except *Enoch* and *Elijah*;[4] and no others will be allowed until the sounding of the last trumpet."[5] Then the pilgrims began to despair in their minds, and especially *Christian*; they looked this way and that way, but no alternative route could be found by which they could avoid the *River*.[6] Then they asked the men if the water was all of the same depth. They replied "No," but could offer no further help other than the comment, "You shall find it deeper or shallower according to your trust in the *King* of the place [*this region*]."[7]

At this the pilgrims resigned themselves to face the water. Upon entering, *Christian* began to sink so that he cried out to his good friend *Hopeful*, "I sink in deep water; the billows go over my head, all his waves go over me! Selah [*Pause*?]."[8]

Then *Hopeful* replied, "Be of good cheer [*be courageous*], my brother, for I feel the bottom and it is firm." Then said *Christian*, "Ah my friend, the sorrows of death have totally compassed [*surrounded*] me, so that I shall not see the land that flows with milk and honey."[9] And with that a great darkness and sense of horror fell upon *Christian* so that he could not see ahead of him.[10] Here, to a large degree, he also lost his senses so that he was unable to remember or talk intelligently about any of those sweet refreshments that he had experienced while traveling on pilgrimage. Rather all of his present talk tended to reveal the present terror of his mind and the fear that he would perish in that *River* and never gain entrance into the *Celestial City*. Here also, those who were able to stand by observed that he was greatly troubled with thoughts about the sins that he had committed, both before and after he became a pilgrim. It was

---

4 *Gen. 5:21-24; II Kings 2:1-11; Heb. 11:5.*

5 I Cor. 15:51-52.

6 *Ps. 55:4; 88:3-9.*

7 Angels are not able to offer comfort through death. *Matt. 9:29.*

8 *Ps. 42:7; 69:1-2; 88:7; Jonah 2:3.*

9 Christians have different experiences at the hour of death.

10 *Ps. 18:4-5; 116:3.*

also noticed that he was disturbed with visions of hobgoblins [*demons*] and evil spirits; his words would reflect this over and over again.

Therefore *Hopeful* struggled here in his attempts to keep his brother's head above water; yes sometimes *Christian* would seem to have sunk down for good, and then after a short while he would rise again seeming half dead. *Hopeful* would also attempt to comfort him, saying, "Brother, I see the gate, and men standing nearby to welcome us." But *Christian* would answer, "It is you, it is you they are waiting for; you have been hopeful ever since I first knew you." "And so have you," said *Hopeful* to *Christian*. "Ah brother," replied *Christian*, "surely if I was right [*with the King*] he would come to my rescue; but on account of my sins, he has brought me to this snare to abandon me."

Then said *Hopeful*, "My brother, you have quite forgotten the text where it speaks of the wicked, 'There is no band [*pain*] in their death, but their strength is firm; they are not troubled as other men, neither are they plagued like other men.'[11] These troubles and distresses that you are experiencing in these waters are no indication that *God* has abandoned you; rather they are sent to test you as to whether you will recall to mind evidences of his past goodness, and now rely upon him in the midst of your present trials."

Then I saw in my dream that *Christian* was in deep thought for a while, so that *Hopeful* spoke to him further, "Be of good cheer [*courageous*], *Jesus Christ* makes you whole." And with that, *Christian* exclaimed with a loud voice, "Oh I see him again! And he tells me, 'When you pass through the waters, I will be with you, and through the rivers, they will not overflow you.'"[12] Then they both took courage, with the result that the enemy then became as still as a stone,[13] until they had fully crossed over. Therefore *Christian* now discovered solid ground to stand upon; and so it followed that the rest of the *River* was found to be shallow. And thus they both crossed over.

---

11 Ps. 73:4-5.

12 Isa. 43:1-2.

13 *Exod. 15:16.*

35

CHRISTIAN AND HOPEFUL ARE WELCOMED INTO HEAVEN

NOW upon the bank of the *River* on the other side, *Christian* and *Hopeful* again saw the two shining men waiting to welcome them. Therefore, having come up out of the *River*, these men saluted and greeted them saying, "We are ministering spirits sent forth to serve those who shall be heirs of salvation."[1] Thus they proceeded towards the gate. Now you should note that the *City* stood upon a mighty *Hill*,[2] though the pilgrims ascended that *Hill* with ease because they had these two men to lead them up by holding their arms; also they had left their mortal garments behind them in the *River*, for though they went in with them, yet they came out without them.[3] Therefore they continued to climb here with much agility and speed, even though the foundation upon which the *City* was built was higher than the clouds. So they went up through the regions of the air, sweetly talking as they went, being comforted because they had safely crossed the *River* and were being escorted by such glorious companions.

The conversation that they had with the *Shining Ones* was about the glory of the place, who told them that the beauty and glory of it was simply inexpressible. They further explained that there is to be found *Mount Zion*, the *Heavenly Jerusalem*, the innumerable company of angels, and the spirits of just men made perfect.[4] Moreover, they explained, "You are now going to the paradise of *God*, in which you shall see the *Tree of Life* and therefore eat of its never-fading fruit.[5] And when you arrive there you shall be given white robes, and every day you shall

---

1 *Luke 16:22; Heb. 1:14.*

2 *Isa. 2:2-4; Mic. 4:1-2.*

3 *I Cor. 15:53-57; II Cor. 5:1-10.*

4 Heb. 12:22-24; Rev. 2:7; 3:4.

5 *Gen. 3:22-24; Rev. 22:2.*

walk and talk with the *King* for all the days of eternity. There you shall not see former things such as you saw when you inhabited the lower region upon *Earth*, that is sorrow, sickness, affliction and death, for these former things will have passed away.[6] Rather you are now going to reside with *Abraham*, *Isaac*, *Jacob* and the prophets, men who *God* took away from the evil to come, for they are resting upon their beds, each one walking in his righteousness."[7]

Then *Christian* and *Hopeful* asked, "What will we be occupied with in such a holy place?" To this was given the answer, "There you will receive the comfort that results from your toil, and have joy in place of your sorrow; you must reap what you have sown, even the fruit of all your prayers and tears and sufferings for the *King* along the way.[8] In that place you will wear crowns of gold and enjoy the perpetual sight and visions of the *Holy One*, for there you shall see him as he is."[9]

"There also you shall continually serve him with praise, with shouting and thanksgiving, that is he whom you desired to serve in the world, though with much difficulty, on account of the weakness of your flesh.[10] There your eyes shall be delighted with seeing, and your ears with hearing, the pleasant voice of the *Mighty One*.[11] There you shall enjoy your friends again, that is those who arrived before you; and there you shall also joyfully welcome everyone who follows after you into this holy place. There also you will be clothed with glory and majesty, and appropriately equipped to ride forth with the *King of Glory*."

"When he shall come with the sound of trumpets in the clouds, as upon the wings of the wind, you shall come with him; and when he shall sit upon the throne of judgment, you shall sit next to him; yes, and when he shall pass sentence upon all the workers of iniquity, whether they be angels or men, you shall

---

6 Rev. 21:1-4.

7 Isa. 57:1-2; 65:14; *Matt. 7:11.*

8 Gal. 6:7.

9 I John 3:2.

10 *Matt. 19:28; 26:41; Rom. 6:19; Gal. 4:13.*

11 *Isa. 30:29; 60:16; 64:4; I Cor. 2:9.*

also have a voice in that judgment because they were his and your enemies.[12] Also when he shall again return to the *City*, you shall go with him, with the sound of trumpets, and be with him forever."[13]

Now while they were drawing near to the gate, behold a company of the heavenly host came out to meet them. To this multitude the *Shining Ones* spoke, "These are the men that have loved our *Lord* when they were in the world, and have left all for his holy name, and he has sent us to fetch them, and thus far have we brought them on their desired journey, that they may now go in and look their *Redeemer* in the face with joy."[14] Then the heavenly host gave a great shout saying, "Blessed are they that are called to the marriage supper of the *Lamb*."[15]

At this time there also came to meet them, several of the *King's* trumpeters, clothed in shining white apparel, who, with loud melodious noises, made even the heavens to echo with their sound. These trumpeters saluted *Christian* and his companion with ten thousand welcomes from the world; and this they did with shouting and the sound of trumpets.

This completed, they surrounded them on every side; some went ahead, some behind, and some on the right hand and some on the left, as a guard through the upper regions, continually sounding as they went with melodious noise in lofty notes. So this sight appeared, to any who could observe, as if *Heaven* itself had come down to meet them. Therefore they walked on together, and as they walked these trumpeters would often, with joyful sound, the composition of their music, and looks and gestures, signify to *Christian* and his friend just how welcome to them was their company, and how happy they were to have met them. And now were these two pilgrims as if in *Heaven*, in fact before they came to it, being consumed with the sight of angels and the hearing of their melodious notes.

Here also they were now able to view the *City* itself, and they thought they heard all the bells inside pealing to welcome them

---

12 Dan. 7:9-10; I Cor. 6:2-3; I Thess. 4:13-16; *II Tim. 2:12*; Jude 14.

13 *Rev. 22:5.*

14 *I Cor. 13:12.*

15 Rev. 19:9.

inside;[16] but above all was their rapturous anticipation, the warm and joyful thoughts that they had about their dwelling there with such heavenly company, and that for ever and ever. Oh, with what tongue or pen could their glorious joy be sufficiently expressed! And thus they came up to the gate.

Now when they had come up to the gate, there was inscribed over it, in letters of gold, "Blessed are they that do his commandments, that they may have rightful access to the *Tree of Life*, and may enter in through the gates into the *City*."[17] Then I saw in my dream that the *Shining Ones* directed the pilgrims to call out at the gate, which, having done so, some from above looked over the top, namely *Enoch*, *Moses*, and *Elijah*.[18] The angels then addressed them: "These pilgrims have come from the *City of Destruction* for the love that they have for the *King* of this place"; and then each one of the pilgrims delivered up his certificate [*scroll*], that which he had received at the beginning; these therefore were brought before the *King* who, when he had read them, said, "Where are these men?" In reply it was explained, "They are standing outside the gate." The *King* then commanded that the gate be opened so that, as he declared, "The righteous nation that keeps the truth may enter in."[19]

Now I saw in my dream that these two men went in through the gate; and behold, as they entered they were transfigured, and they were dressed with apparel that shone like gold.[20] They were also met by those who gave them harps and crowns; the harps to add praise, and the crowns as tokens of honor bestowed.[21]

Then I heard in my dream that all the bells in the *City* again rang out for joy; and that it was said to the pilgrims, "Enter into

---

16 *This is reminiscent of Bunyan's early experience as a bell-ringer.*

17 Rev. 22:14.

18 *These saints identify the three who walked at the top of the Palace that the Persevering Valiant Pilgrim strove to enter.*

19 Isa. 26:2.

20 *I Cor. 15:42-44, 51-53.*

21 *Rev. 4:4; 5:8.*

the joy of your *Lord*."[22] I also heard the men themselves sing, and that with loud voices saying, "Blessing, honor, glory, and power, be to him who sits upon the throne, and to the *Lamb* for ever and ever."[23]

Now just as the gates were opened to let in the men, I looked in after them; and behold, the *City* shone like the sun; the streets also were paved with gold, and on them walked many men with crowns on their heads, palms in their hands, and golden harps with which to sing praises.[24]

Also among the inhabitants there were those that had wings, and they responded in praise one to the other without ceasing, saying "Holy, holy, holy, is the *Lord*."[25] And after that they closed the gates; and because of what I had seen of this glorious sight, I [*Bunyan*] wished myself to have been inside among them.

Heavern's Gate opened

---

22 *Matt. 25:23.*

23 Rev. 5:13-14.

24 *Rev. 7:9-10; 15:2-4.*

25 *Isa. 6:3; Rev. 4:8.*

36

THE FEARFUL END OF IGNORANCE

NOW while I [*Bunyan*] was gazing upon all these things, I turned my head to look back and saw *Ignorance* come up to the bank of the *River*: but he was able to quickly reach the other side, and without half the difficulty that *Christian* and *Hopeful* had experienced.[1] For it then happened that he found in that place a ferryman named *Vain-hope* who, with his boat, was able to transport him across.

So, as was the case with the others I had watched, he ascended the *Hill* and approached the gate of the *Celestial City*, except that he traveled alone; neither did any man meet him and offer the least encouragement.

When he had reached the gate, he looked up at the writing that was inscribed above; and then he began to knock, supposing that he would quickly be permitted to gain entrance. But the men who peered at him over the top of the gate first asked, "From where have you come? And what is it that you desire?"

So *Ignorance* replied, "I have eaten and have drunk in the presence of the *King*, and he has taught in our streets."[2] Then they asked him for his certificate [*scroll*], so that they might go to the *King* and show it to him. So he fumbled in his chest pocket and yet was unable to find anything. Then they further inquired, "Have you none?" But the man answered not so much as a word.[3] So they told the *King*, but he would not come down to see him. Instead, he commanded the same two *Shining Ones*, who had previously conducted *Christian* and *Hopeful* to the *City*, to seize *Ignorance*, bind him hand and foot, and carry him away.[4] Then they took him up and carried him through the air

---

1 *Ps. 73:3-4.*

2 *Luke 13:26-27.*

3 *Matt. 22:12; Rom. 3:19.*

4 *Matt. 22:13.*

to the door that I had earlier seen in the side of the *Hill* below the *Delectable Mountains*, and despatched him there.[5]

Then I saw that there was a way to *Hell* even from the gates of *Heaven*, as well as from the *City of Destruction*.[6] So I awoke, and behold it was a dream.

Ignorance

5 *Rev. 20:11-15.*

6 *Matt. 26:25.*

THE CONCLUSION

Now reader, I have told my dream to thee [*you*];
See if you can interpret it to me;
Or to yourself, or neighbor: but take heed
Of misinterpreting: for that, instead
Of doing good, will but yourself abuse:
By misinterpreting evil ensues.

Take heed also, that you be not extreme,
In playing with the outside of my dream:
Nor let my figure, or similitude,
Put you into a laughter or a feud;
Leave this for boys and fools; but as for thee [*you*],
Do yourself the substance of my matter see.[1]

Put by the curtains, look within my veil;
Turn up my metaphors and do not fail:
There, if you seek them, such things to find,
As will be helpful to an honest mind.

What of my dross you find there, be bold
To throw away, but yet preserve the gold.
What if my apple be wrapped up in ore?
None throws away the apple for the core:
But if you shall cast all away as vain,
I know not but 'twill make me dream again.

THE END

---

1 *Carefully consider what is the biblical substance of Bunyan's dream.*

A FURTHER DEFENSE

Some say the *Pilgrim's Progress* is not mine,
Insinuating as if I would shine
In name and fame by the worth of another,
Like some made rich by robbing of their brother.
Or that so fond I am of being sire,
I'll father bastards; or, if need require,
I'll tell a lie in print to get applause.
I scorn it: *John* such dirt-heap never was,
Since *God* converted him. Let this suffice
To show why I my *Pilgrim* patronize.

It came from my own heart, so to my head,
And there into my fingers trickled;
Then to my pen, from where immediately
On paper I did dribble it daintily.

Manner and matter too was all my own,
Nor was it unto any mortal known
Till I had done it; nor did any then
By books, by wits, by tongues, or hand, or pen,
Add five words to it, or write half a line
Thereof: the whole, and every part, is mine.

John Bunyan, *The Holy War*

INDEX

The Mission Statement of Reformation Press

The ministry of Reformation Press was established to glorify The Lord Jesus Christ and to be used by Him to expand and edify the kingdom of God while we occupy and anticipate Christ's glorious return. Reformation Press will seek to accomplish this mission by publishing Gospel literature which is biblically faithful, relevant, and practically applicable to many of the serious spiritual needs of mankind upon the verge of a new millennium. To do so we will always seek to boldly incorporate the truths of Scripture, especially those which were largely articulated as a body of theology during The Protestant Reformation of the sixteenth century and ensuing years. We gladly join our voice in the proclamations of— *Scripture Alone, Faith Alone, Grace Alone, Christ Alone, and God's Glory Alone!*

Our ministry seeks the blessing of our God as we seek His face to both confirm and support our labors for Him. Our prayers for this work can be summarized by two verses from the Book of Psalms:

> ***"And let the beauty of the LORD our God be upon us, And establish the work of our hands for us; Yes, establish the work of our hands." —Psalm 90:17***

> ***"Not unto us, O LORD, not unto us, but to your name give glory." —Psalm 115:1***

Reformation Press is a not-for-profit (501 C3) institution and therefore can and does appreciates monetary donations from anyone who shares our burden and vision for publishing literature combining sound Bible doctrine and practical exhortation in an age when too few so-called Christian publications do the same. All donations will be recognized by a tax-deductible receipt. We thank you in advance for any assistance you can give us in our labors to fulfill this important mission. May God bless you.

For a catalog of additional
great Christian books
including other titles
by Dr. Barry E. Horner
contact us by any
of the following ways:

write us at:

Reformation Press
160 37th Street
Lindenhurst, NY 11757

call us at:

516. 956. 0606

find us on the internet at:

www. reformationpress.com or
www.greatchristianbooks.com

email us at:

reformationpress@email.com